THE LINCOLNSHIRE AGRICULTURAL SOCIETY

The Rt. Hon. the Earl of Yarborough,
President of the Lincolnshire Agricultural Society
at its inception in 1869.

The
Lincolnshire
Agricultural
Society

Its predecessors and its development.
County Societies from the era of strip farming,
to Shows in the yards of inns,
their comprehensive growth, to the permanent
County Showground.

Published by the Society
in the year of their one hundredth
Annual Show, 1983

Researched and written by J. G. Ruddock
for the Lincolnshire Agricultural Society
Lincolnshire Showground, Grange-de-Lings, Lincoln

L·63

©The Lincolnshire Agricultural Society
Printed by J. W. Ruddock & Sons Ltd, Lincoln

The NARRATIVE

ILLUSTRATIONS

FOREWORD

by the Rt. Hon. the Earl of Ancaster, K.C.V.O., T.D.
President of the Society

The development and progress of the Lincolnshire Agricultural Society over the years has followed and been largely determined by the changes brought about in the Agricultural Industry as a whole and within our own County in particular. From its beginnings nearly 200 years ago, through a period of consolidation during the late 19th century and the early part of this century, up to the high degree of mechanisation and specialisation we find today, the Lincolnshire Show has portrayed the changes in the Agricultural Industry and all that is best within our County.

The farming community of Lincolnshire can rightly boast of the very great contribution they have made over the years, especially during two World Wars, to the well being and wealth of our Country. They can also be proud of the way in which the Annual Lincolnshire Show has always kept abreast of the times and reflected the ever changing pattern of Agriculture both within the Country and our County. In writing this History of the Society to commemorate the Centenary of the Show the Author describes this parallel development of our County Agricultural Show over the years. Mention is made of many to whom the Society and Show, and the Agricultural Industry, owe a great debt for their work and foresight.

It is a great pleasure to commend the book to you and to wish the Society continuing success in the years to come.

The Earlier Scene

The need to foster agricultural development led to the growth of Agricultural Societies in the eighteenth century. It was a period which included the demise of strip farming, with its disputes and time-wasting travel between separated lands. Intermittent disuse of land as fallow ceased with the introduction of rotation of crops. Though from as far back as the fourteenth century horses had sometimes been substituted for oxen for efficiency, they had not yet replaced them. But more effective horse-drawn implements had been developed. Seeds were being more carefully selected.

William Pitt formed the Board of Agriculture in 1793, because of the Napoleonic Wars, the cutting off of trade, a series of bad harvests, high prices, and in the context of his exaggerated fear of social unrest. One of its purposes was to encourage the formation of agricultural societies. This explains why their rules and regulations throughout the country were virtually the same. (The Board ceased in 1822).

Agricultural improvements became fashionable with landowners, with, of course, variations in intensity throughout the land. This had followed the knowledge of methods in Italy and France — four-course rotation which resulted in more crops, more animal food, more manure. Jethro Tull was one who published designs and uses of implements — the activation of his seed drill being based on the working parts of an organ — and he discussed stubble burning, and its use by the ancient Romans. More or less by eye and contemplative appreciation selective breeding of sheep and cattle had their proponents. Thomas Stone, land surveyor, of Gray's Inn, London, reported to the Board of Agriculture, in 1794, that tenantry in Lincolnshire was mostly on annual leases, which gave no incitement to improvement, no security, and no reward. He urged Gentlemen to grant appropriate leases as in some other counties, "rather than leave improvement to the active zeal of Agricultural Societies". In this era a Lincolnshire Agricultural Society was formed in 1796. The progression of societies is as follows:

The First LINCOLNSHIRE AGRICULTURAL SOCIETY, 1796 to 1799.

Formed for the projection of agricultural matters by discussion. *Based at Folkingham.*

The LINCOLNSHIRE (Division of Lindsey) AGRICULTURAL SOCIETY, 1799 to 1812.

The first Society in the County having the policy of holding a Stock Show, with Labourers' and Servants' awards. *Based at Barton-on-Humber.*

The second LINCOLNSHIRE AGRICULTURAL SOCIETY, 1819 to 1847. *Based at Lincoln.*

(In 1840 this L.A.S. and the following N.L.A.S., agreed to merge, but the decision was reversed).

The NORTH LINCOLNSHIRE AGRICULTURAL SOCIETY, 1836 to 1868. *Based at Brigg.*

The SOUTH LINCOLNSHIRE AGRICULTURAL ASSOCIATION, 1868. *Based at Grantham/Sleaford.*

(On the 8th January, 1869, in general meeting, the last two ratified their committee agreements to amalgamate; thus the present LINCOLNSHIRE AGRICULTURAL SOCIETY came into being. While it is the third Society of this name, it is the only one which has had the benefit of developing communication in all its forms, to enable it to have County-wide influence). *Based at Lincoln.*

The first Lincolnshire Agricultural Society, 1796 to 1799. (Folkingham)

"On February 29th, 1796, there was established at Folkingham a Society, very properly called the Lincolnshire Agricultural Society, being the first in the County". Thus it was stated in the General View of the Agriculture of the

LINCOLNSHIRE

Agricultural Society.

A MEETING of the Members is particularly requested, on WEDNESDAY the eighth Day of MAY next, at the GREY HOUND INN, in FALKINGHAM, to take into Confideration feveral important Matters, particularly interefting to the Members of this Society.

HENRY HOYTE, Secretary.

N. B. Dinner on the Table precifely at two o'Clock.

LINCOLNSHIRE.

BREED OF STOCK.

WHEREAS feveral Gentlemen refident within the Divifion of Lindfey, are defirous of promoting the Improvement of the Breed of Stock,

Notice is hereby given,

That a MEETING is intended to be holden at the WHITE HART INN, in MARKET RAISIN, on TUESDAY the 16th of APRIL next, at eleven o'Clock in the Forenoon; when and where all Perfons wifhing to join in the Undertaking, are requefted to attend.

By Order,

THOs. MARRIS.

BARTON-UPON-HUMBER, *March* 30, 1799.

County of Lincoln as drawn up for the Board of Agriculture in 1799. Folkingham was then the Sessions centre of Kesteven. The Society began with thirteen members, their names being: Rasor, Burton, Oliver, Holderness, Newcomb, Dawson, Cragg, Henley, Wayan, Maples, Newton, Summers, and Hoyte, who was Secretary.

They were practical farmers connected together to converse about improvements. It became more formal, with topics put forward and resolutions made upon them. Some business was achieved:

Resolved by the members present that curved lands (strips) should be reduced to level and straight ones.

Resolved the best sized lands adapted to farming are four to five yards wide.

Resolved that tares are the properest method of producing food for sheep in the Spring, after turnips have been expended — unless the land admits the sowing of rye, then feed that and leave it as a crop.

11

DIVISION OF LINDSEY.

AGRICULTURAL SOCIETY.

AT a MEETING of the Committee appointed by this Society, lately holden at the Talbot Inn, in Caistor, in the County of Lincoln, the following PREMIUMS were ordered to be offered for Cattle and Sheep bred within the said Division, and to be shewn at CAISTOR aforesaid, on WEDNESDAY the 27th Day of AUGUST, 1800.

	£.	s.
For the best Shearling Ram —	5	5
Second best Ditto —	2	2
For the best two-shear Ram —	5	5
Second best Ditto — —	2	2
For the best Bull, not exceeding three Years old when shewn — —	5	5
Second best Ditto — —	2	2
For the best aged Bull — —	5	5
Second best Ditto —	2	2
For the best two-years old Heifer —	5	5
Second best Ditto —	2	2
For the best Boar, not exceeding two Years old when shewn — —	2	2
Second best Ditto —	1	1
For the best six Shearling Wethers —	3	3
For the best six two-shear Wethers	3	3
For the best six Gimmers —	6	6

N. B. These Premiums will be decided at the first Meeting, and Certificates of the Ages required. —No Stock to be entitled to the Premiums without full Proof of it's being bred by the Claimant. —The Stock not confined to be kept on vegetable Food; only a Declaration will be required at the Time of shewing, in what Manner the same has been kept; and Persons intending to become Candidates, are desired to give 14 Days Notice, in Writing, to the Secretary.

Also the following Premiums were ordered to be offered the same Day, for Persons residing in the said Division, viz.

	£.	s.
To the Labourer in Husbandry, who has brought up the most numerous Family without parochial Assistance —	2	2
To the Labourer in Husbandry, who has worked for one Master, or on one Farm the longest Time, he working for such Master, or on that Farm at the Time he makes his Claim — —	1	1
To the Male Servant, who has lived the longest Time with any one Master or Mistress in Husbandry — —	1	1
To the Female Servant, who has lived the longest Time with any one Master or Mistress in Husbandry —	1	1

N. B. These Premiums will be disposed of at the annual Meeting; and Candidates must give Notice, in Writing, with the necessary Information to the Secretary, before the said 27th Day of August; but no Claim will be admitted but for those who have lived at least seven Years in each of the above Situations.
By Order,

THO. MARRIS, Secretary.

Advertisement for the first Stock Show in Lincolnshire with premiums for Sheep, Cattle, and Labourers and Servants, as advertised for the 27th August, 1800, at Caistor.
(Lincoln, Rutland & Stamford Mercury)

There were diverse opinions on Halt in sheep, but it was generally agreed that pastures kept neat, and animals well pared in Spring were preventives. Members were asked to try measures and report back on the comparative effectiveness of straw manure for heavy soils and spit manure for light soils for an ensuing crop of turnips.

Hopeful as was its title, the life of the Society was less than four years. Local societies for farming activities came into being, having scant connection with each other, and they adopted local names more in accordance with their area of influence.

The Lincolnshire (Division of Lindsey) Agricultural Society 1799 to 1812.
(Barton-on-Humber)

The desire of gentlemen to improve the breed of stock led to a meeting being held on 16th April 1799 at the White Hart Inn at Market Rasen. It was in the first sixteen societies in the country. The advertisement in the Lincoln, Rutland and Stamford Mercury calling the meeting was strangely next to the one for the last meeting of the Society based at Folkingham. Mr Thomas Marris, of Barton-on-Humber, the Secretary of the new Society, would doubtless have known of this Kesteven venture of some three years' existence, but hardly of its forthcoming demise. This Society had stronger backing, and Lord Yarborough was the President. Its purpose was more likely to gain support from practical farmers. They began their first show of 27th August 1800 at Caistor, with premiums for Rams, Bulls, Heifer, Boar, Wethers and Gimmers, to have been bred by the claimants. Labourers and servants were offered awards in this Show only. Twelve shows were held, all for stock only after the first one. They were in effect competitions held in inn yards, as the Talbot at Caistor, White Hart at Market Rasen, Bull at Horncastle, New Kings Head at Louth, White Lion at Wragby. Entrants were widespread from Barton to East Keal. It was individually run, the only committee being the one called annually to decide on the rules "to settle the mode of keeping stock intended to be shown". It was always confirmed to be "not confined to be kept on vegetable foods only".

The list of competitors grew but their number was never large. Long-wool rams were represented, but the system for them was by breeders advertising show days on their own farms. Machinery was ignored, though in Lincolnshire by 1807 there were a few thrashing, dressing and shaking machines powered by horses, made by William Forge of Hull. The Show of 1811 took place after a short postponement, and proved to be the last one. The next year the Society ceased.

Some of the same families in this Society were to be active in the later North Lincolnshire Agricultural Society of 1836; such as the Lords Yarborough, the Boucheretts, Dixons, Skipworths, and the Turnors.

The second Lincolnshire Agricultural Society, 1819 to 1847 (Lincoln)

The year 1819 saw revival of interest in having a Society, when Gentlemen, farmers and others met on the 21st of April in Lincoln at the Rein Deer Inn. In Guildhall Street, this was the usual venue of such as the justices of local wapentakes (hundreds). It was in response to an advertisement in the Lincoln, Rutland and Stamford Mercury, apparently sponsored by the City of Lincoln. The Mayor, Robert Featherby, was in the chair.

The various departments of breeding of cattle and cultivation of land were uppermost in their final resolution. "Their great utility could only be appreciated and rewarded by the public spirit of Agriculturists generally espousing and recognizing the same. Effectiveness was by the combination of Landed Proprietors and Tenantry."

They noted that: the effectuation of their great and important object was to be the projection of a "Cattle Show and Agricultural Society" — in the City of Lincoln — for the general benefit of the County of Lincoln. A committee of forty-nine was formed to frame rules. The first members of the Society represented a fair spread from the north of the County and the Wolds to near Grantham. The Lord Lieutenant, Earl Brownlow, was to be asked to be President. The County members of Parliament were asked for support. The meeting had run to a session on the next day.

The Mayor duly convened the next meeting for the 5th July, 1819. It resolved that "a society be now formed". It took a few months for the name to settle down — this resolution called it "The Lincolnshire Agricultural Society, or Annual Cattle Show". In a fortnight the name was the "Lincolnshire Society for the Encouragement of Agriculture and Industry". After that they settled for "Lincolnshire Agricultural Society".

Lord Brownlow's acceptance of the position of President was dated twenty-three days after the day of the first meeting. In the days when the horse was the fastest means of land transport it is surprising that he apologized for the delay — no disrespect was meant — but he had just left Belton and the papers had been forwarded to him and had got mixed up. He would feel the greatest satisfaction and could not hesitate to accept, "notwithstanding the sense I entertain of my own inadequate acquaintance with Agricultural Concerns".

The list of those invited to be Vice-Presidents contains many names still known in the County today or in recent memory:

Lord Yarborough, Lord Gwydyr, Pelham, Banks, Robinson, Trollop, Thorold, Whichcote, Anderson, Nelthorpe, Sheffield, Gordon, Heron, Cholmeley, Welby, Manners, Reynardson, Chaplin, Ellison, Sibthorp, Tomline, Bouchcrett, Dalton, Goulton, Vyner, Turnor, Cracroft, Heneage, Lister, Reeve, Mainwaring, Johnson, Hutton, Weston, Livesey, Tennyson, and ex-officio the Mayor of Lincoln.

The basic subscription was one guinea — paid annually in arrear.

Two enduring statements were made at the 16th July 1819 meeting — that there was hardly any object of rational improvement which premiums (prizes) would not influence — and that the Society would operate in proportion to the support they would receive, for the prosperity of the County and the

15

good of the Community at large. Agriculture did of course affect everyone's livelihood. Such manufactures as existed were related to farming and produce. Scunthorpe was then undeveloped, and Grimsby had by no means taken its present place.

Twenty uninterrupted years

The first year there were 107 subscribers. Within months they were sanguine of the full effect of the institution of the Society, and decided to publish the fact.

Some prominent persons declined their invited Vice-Presidency, however, such as General Manners; new ones included Sir Gilbert Heathcote, the Hon. and Reverend the Champion Dymoke, the reactionary Charles Delaet Waldo Sibthorp (who sometimes took the chair), Christopher Nevile Noel, the Reverend Peregrine Curtois, and Dr John Willis (who had treated George III).

The annual show, referred to as "the Anniversary" was held in a paddock in Lincoln, just south of the river, not far from the stock market of that time. In spite of its name it was a localised society, as in the state of transport at the time it had to be; but it was assisted by the more prominent gentry from further away. The fens were represented only one year by a prize winning cart stallion from Holbeach Marsh; possibly its tour coincided.

Competition arranged at the Shows was almost all for stock; Cart Stallion, Bull, Milch Cow, Heifer, Ram, Shearing Ram, Two-Shear Ram, Pen of Six Gimmers, Boar and Sow. The premiums were from ten guineas down to one, or plate to their values. Soon Blood Stallion was introduced, and Cart Stallion dropped, but not before one was allowed in even though it had also worked in Rutlandshire. In 1823 the rules were augmented about rams — that they should be fed only on grass, clover, turnips or other roots and vegetables for the four months preceding. No cake, corn, seed or dry food allowed. Mr Francis Brown provided the premium, and this was his rule, following some of the thinking of the time. He later allowed feed on hay and straw.

The Shepherd class concerned the greatest number of lambs reared from not less than two hundred ewes. The three and two guinea prizes represented a few weeks' wages. One year the winner had 603 lambs from 403 ewes.

The labourer who had brought up the largest family without parochial relief would receive five or three guineas for first or second respectively. The winner one year with eleven children (one died at eight years, one at school) and twenty years with his employer was certainly outdone by William Jacklin of Appleby, who had had twenty four, and had brought up eighteen. The grown up offspring were stated always as being placed into service.

Ploughing of half an acre, not less than four to five inches deep, in four hours, with a pair of horses was listed. Held near Lincoln, the entries were local, up to about ten. Three guineas, or plate to the value, down to half a guinea for compensating losing owners. A later change of the rules gave the prizes to the ploughman and not to the farmer.

Agricultural implements were encouraged by a desire to consider "correct statements" of new successful experiments. Fifteen guineas were allocated "if thanks are not enough". The main factors to consider were the simplicity of construction, the smallness of price, and a fair claim to importance. The first year, 1820, brought a Gramminator (pertaining to grass) and an essay thereon from Mr Whitworth of Caistor. He received thanks, not having given due notice. Three years later the Society was informed of the successful planting of Ray (Rye) and other grasses by this machine.

Over the years were demonstrated a wheel-drill by Spink of Scampton; a hand-thrashing machine of Chambers of Lincoln (paid £10.10.0.); a ridge drill to sow two rows at once and to dust the plant with lime when attacked by the fly. Other drills appeared, with multiple coulters, multiple tines, to deposit manure with turnip seed, and one with a stirrer in the bone box. In 1840 Richard Hornsby of Grantham received an award for his two-row drop-sill machine, already patented.

The show seems to have been in the character of a competition for those who were usual attenders at Lincoln markets. Its influence was not widespread, nor did the entrants change much. One servant candidate won three years running, so that premium was stopped. In 1828 with several machines shown none were deserving. The next year two awards for implements were given — one to a woman, Lucy Barret of Lincoln. Few great landholders attended, however, and this lack of appreciation and stimulus was regretted. From 1835 the Corporation of Lincoln discontinued its support.

The North Lincolnshire Agricultural Society, 1836 to 1868 (Brigg)

On Thursday, 13th October 1836, a public meeting had been held in the Town Hall, Brigg, following an advertisement. By resolution the Society was there and then established, and it forthwith dominated the County scene. It is the major ancestor of the Society of today. There were already existing local Agricultural Associations in Barton, Grimsby, Caistor, Winterton and Brigg — the new Society was not directly connected with them. It seems, however, that it was founded by their representatives, because their secretaries were shortly asked about their areas, and members were to be canvassed through them. Personal approaches to prospects were soon deemed to be better.

The Honourable C. A. W. Pelham, M.P., was in the chair. The resolutions were long and clear, appointments immediate and the structure and policy laid down. The object was to promote improvement in the various branches of the rural economy — stock — culture of the soil — implements — corn — seeds — vegetables — manure and its application. It was the standard pattern. Emulation was to be the powerful means of effecting such object, and premiums and public competition.

Honesty, industry and economy encouraged amongst the laboring classes would promote their happiness and comfort, with countenance and sympathy from their superiors, to cement the bonds which unite society.

18

NORTH LINCOLNSHIRE
AGRICULTURAL SOCIETY.

THE FIRST MEETING

OF THIS SOCIETY,

FOR THE EXHIBITION OF STOCK,

AWARDING OF PREMIUMS, &c.

WILL BE HELD AT BRIGG, ON THURSDAY THE 28th SEPTEMBER NEXT.

PREMIUMS:

	£.	s.	d.
First Class.—To the Owner of the best STALLION, for getting Hunters,	5	0	
Second.—To the Owner of the best ditto, for getting Hacknies,			
Third.—To the Owner of the best ditto, for getting Coach-Horses,			
Fourth.—To the Owner of the best ditto, for getting Draugh* purposes,			
Fifth.—To the Owner of the best BULL,			

Notice of 1837 of the first Show of the North Lincolnshire Agricultural Society, which grew in strength through its policy of moving from town to town. (Lincolnshire Archives)

Rules and regulations followed; the committee elected; subscription books opened. There were thirty-two Vice-Presidents, including the Hon. C. A. W. Pelham, M.P., J. G. Corbett, Esq., M.P., Sir John Nelthorpe, Bt., Sir M. J. Cholmeley, Bt., Sir W. A. Ingilby, Bt., G. F. Heneage, Esq., Henry Thorold, Esq., Richard Thorold, Esq., Edward Weston, Esq., R. C. Elwes, Esq., Hickman Bacon, Esq., John Dixon, Esq. Much preparation must have been done. Within a fortnight it was decided that the first Exhibition was to be at Brigg on 28th September, 1837, in the paddock occupied by Mr Francis Bennett at the East End of Bigby Street. Some thought it to be a late date, but it was appropriate for corn, seeds and bulbous roots. There was insistence that stock should be exhibited in its natural state, not overfed as was the vogue of late. The Dinner Tent was unfortunately erected upon Mrs Gilliat's Bowling Green, and she had to be compensated.

The Show was described as "for the Exhibition of Stock". For some years it was predominantly so, and thought of as such. Included, however, were premiums for servants and labourers, and for seeds. There were sweepstakes on stock and horse classes, the entrants contributing a sovereign to the pool, the winner taking all. As to Implements of Husbandry, there was but one premium, five pounds for the best new or improved one. This single item was the unwitting harbinger of so much forthcoming agricultural and show development.

Some questioned the utility of the Society, but after the first show there was £75.10.2. in hand, and 180 subscribers paying £226.10. For the next show 2,000 entry tickets were to be printed. The Rt. Hon. Lord Worsley was particularly mentioned for his influence, support, attendance and entry of stock.

They knew they had not done much yet to promote improvement in cultivation, and particularly diseases of Sheep and Beast had not received enough attention. As to the latter, the committee felt that it showed great lack of judgment in obtaining valuable animals and yet neglecting the means of preserving them.

The second and the North Societies unite and separate

After two of the North Lincolnshire Shows and a poor one of their own, the committee and others in Lincoln gave it as their opinion (16th August 1839) that "the existence of so many Agricultural Societies in the County, particularly this Society and that of the North Lincolnshire is detrimental to each other". It was "highly desirable that the same be united". (There were about fifteen other Ploughing, Labourers, and Local Societies). The Hon. A. L. Melville was the chairman. A deputation of four was agreed. They sought no more in the detail than Lincoln should have a show next year and every five years, which could be broken for the English (later the "Royal") Agricultural Society; the Vice-Presidents to be combined; the committees to co-operate this year. Members of both Societies were to be informed.

The N.L.A.S. stipulated that "they could on no account depart from the perambulating principle". Should union take place, the City of Lincoln would have benefit of that principle. The N.L.A.S. committee met again three weeks later but no communication had been received. Five weeks later, the same. Three weeks after, the same again. After seven weeks further the reply had come from Lincoln. A joint meeting at Caistor was inconvenient, so it was adjourned to Market Rasen (Lincoln would have preferred Spital, by Caenby Corner). Meanwhile both had separately finalised their agreement.

The N.L.A.S. first wished to add that premiums should go to the English Agricultural Society when they had a show locally. This proved easy to accept, and "the Union of the two Societies now takes place" was resolved on 18th January 1840. The Earl of Yarborough of the N.L.A.S. was to be requested to continue as President. The Earl Brownlow of the L.A.S. was thanked for his attention and support, and it was hoped that he would continue with the united society. C. Chaplin, Esq. was asked to explain the circumstances to his Lordship. This was clear acceptance of the N.L.A.S. formula of moving the Annual Show from town to town, so as to gain co-operation, and thus not to overdo the local need and interest. However, at their 25th February 1840 meeting the N.L.A.S. heard that there was a hitch between the L.A.S. and their President Earl Brownlow. He had refused his agreement. The N.L.A.S. resolved that they were sorry but they could not disturb the arrangement.

At the end of March the N.L.A.S. in Brigg decided that no means of accommodating the differences respecting the presidency had presented themselves. The Union was made under a misapprehension. To prevent unpleasant feeling and great injury to the Society — Resolved that the Union be dissolved. They proceeded to organise their next show.

The L.A.S. in Lincoln was by then finalising accounts from suppliers, and subscriptions (some were several years out of date). Sharp words about lack of information passed between the Societies' secretaries. Lincoln continued with the idea of union for a few weeks, ignoring their President. They sent out a circular on 23rd April about it as a fact, and their consequent dissolution.

They had made their decisions without consulting Lord Brownlow. As the consequence of meeting him Mr Chaplin was in the chair at a General Meeting of the L.A.S. on 1st May 1840 for the purpose of the Union being dissolved, so that the Society continue its operation as heretofore. The week-old circular about the Union was followed by an immediate one about their continuance. The previous Vice-Presidents, Committee, and Officers were to be requested to continue to the next anniversary. Earl Brownlow was duly asked to continue as President. It was all to carry on, but to have their shows migratory with the different towns participating. Sleaford was suggested as the next one. Clearly it was expected to emulate the N.L.A.S. in the south of the County, and to be as successful. With Lincoln as their main town on the circuit it seemed to be a promising idea. Their 1840 Show was then got together.

The second Lincolnshire Agricultural Society ceases, 1847

The opportunity of the extended area of influence into South Lincolnshire was taken in seeking further Vice-Presidents, such as Earl Winchelsea, Earl Ripon, Colonel Cracroft. The Lord Monson did now join, after earlier refusals. Premiums increased, Hunting horses were brought in, categories of stock were widened. After Sleaford it was to be Lincoln for 1842, to arrange which the meeting on 27th August was strongly attended. Subsequent to the Sleaford Show however, at a meeting at the Green Man Inn, on Navenby Heath, it was reported that the funds stood at only £14.17.9. This was neither basis for increasing their activity, nor for risking another show in a small town. "The success of this Society is very mainly dependent on a large attendance of the County Gentlemen at the Anniversary". This was the secretary's opinion. Being migratory between Lincoln and Sleaford was proving insufficient.

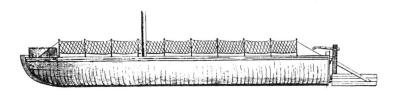

Boat used for conveying sheep by Mr John Cartwright, of Brothertoft, early in the nineteenth century, still the age of water transport. It was fifty two feet long and twelve feet wide. The sheep were lined up along both sides in the hold, with a feeding trough down the centre. A deck was laid, allowing some air to those below, and two further lines of sheep similarly arranged upon it.

(General Review of Lincolnshire Agriculture, 1813)

Boston was not considered because parties in the vicinity were assumed to be very lukewarm. Support was offered if Boston made the invitation.

The Secretary, R. A. Carline of Lincoln, who was honorary, reckoned that one large perambulating society was to be preferred to small local ones. The Sleaford show of 1841 had not been without complaints — for late advertising of premiums — but he had not received the information. And the President had wanted to alter the date because of the General Election. "It was presumptuous to differ, but it was all too far advanced. In fact the election and the candidates' presence would produce stir and excitement". Mr Carline did manage to organise the toasts at the dinner instead of being as usual "dependent on casual gentlemen to speak". He also wrote sharply and at some length in response to an unjustified complaint from Mr Watts of Belton that Lord Brownlow had difficulty in receiving premiums which had been won.

By 1843 he feared for the Society, and wished to ride over to Blankney to see Mr Chaplin before the next meeting. It "would do much good" if he could attend it. Chairmen were becoming difficult to find for Exhibition day. Lord Brownlow was becoming ill, Earl Winchelsea was abroad; Earl Ripon and Weston Cracroft of Hackthorne were notified. The former was unable, the latter was in Herefordshire. In two letters to different places he asked Mr A. Boucherett.

1845 at Sleaford was likely to be the last Anniversary. Smith, Ellison gave a piece of plate value six guineas for the best pen of 20 wether hoggs, perhaps in response to Mr Carline's printed appeal for support to gentlemen having estates. Sir W. Ingilby sent a generous £25, the only real assistance from anybody. The Hon. A. L. Melville wrote from Stoke Rochford that it was no use; "Lincolnshire cannot support two Societies, and the northern one has got too strong a footing". His opinion was influential. He had taken part in county agricultural affairs for a long time, being the manager of the Smith, Ellison Bank. He was also a Vice-President of the N.L.A.S., from its inception, even when "new in the County". On the 20th August matters were at a standstill in the Lincoln office, with no entries received. The next day they arrived — from Sleaford, and the Show would be "much larger than on any former occasion". Mr Carline wrote back: "Without delay look up no end of beast trays".

After this Sleaford Show there was a meeting at the Green Man Inn, not numerously attended. "We all wore rather long faces. Up to £80 in debt. Subscriptions in arrear. Sleaford contributed literally nothing". Mr Chaplin went to Lincoln to see Mr Carline on request, by letter — "not wishing publicly to expose our poverty". The treasurer, Mr C. A. Hayward, gave his report. (He had run it in a personal manner, paying Society bills himself, being reimbursed by cheques on Smith, Ellison & Co. at Lincoln made out to "myself"; not all of them being on Bank forms).

The Society made its contribution to agriculture. The implements included as great a variety and range as any show — from a Lincolnshire wood plough, waggons and carts, to portable thrashing machines. There was stock, but as a Show doubtless it was too frequently in the same place for adequate support. The secretary still put on a front, however, to try and prevent Mr R. Dudding of Panton from resigning.

The Society was consulted in October 1845 as to where a new and improved Cattle Market in Lincoln should be. The existing one was too small, stock was being damaged by standing on the stones of the streets. They decided. It was acted upon — it was there on Monks Road for over a century, having been relocated from Sheep Square (where St. Swithin's Church now stands).

The next year they did not have the money to offer premiums. This Lincolnshire Agricultural Society was dissolved at a small meeting in Lincoln Guildhall on 16th July 1847. They referred to "several" local Agricultural Associations, and to themselves as "the parent Society". Subscriptions in arrear were requested. It was 1850 before the Sleaford balance could be obtained from the administrator there. Excuses were made that he did not know which year subscriptions received were for. "The information could be collected but only Mr Goodall knew, and he'd just been in and had gone out again and it was not known when he would be seen again. If no further word it must be attributed to his absence".

The cessation of the L.A.S. of Lincoln was noted by the N.L.A.S. of Brigg in June 1848 in that there are "now no obstacles to having a Show at Lincoln", which had hitherto been prevented. It was highly desirable, and must be one "commensurate with the high reputation of the city. It was beyond any personal inconvenience".

The North Lincolnshire Society Exhibitions

Represented by the growth of its shows, the North Lincolnshire Agricultural Society established itself strongly. The policy of moving from town to town was effective in their area because of the number which could carry an exhibition every few years — Brigg, Barton, Gainsborough, Louth, Horncastle, Grimsby, Market Rasen, Spilsby and Caistor. (Scunthorpe had still not begun its growth). Alford made a request.

After the 1840 Exhibition the Society felt it was flourishing enough to establish ploughing matches; a premium for the best cultivated garden and the neatest cottage (the Revd. Algernon

Massingberd then paid for these two); and for the longest and largest contribution to a Savings Bank or Friendly Society.

They had been placed in an anomalous position by mutual endeavour to effect a junction with the Lincolnshire Agricultural Society, but their interests had not suffered.

The ultimate growth of the N.L.A.S. was due to the railway communications a dozen years later, enabling more servants and labourers and stock to be brought to the shows, and above all to the burgeoning inventions of implements and steam machinery, again which could be transported and shown. During the nineteenth century mechanical effectiveness multiplied at least by six times. It is as important, though, to accept and use new devices.

At the first show three entrants exhibited dressing machines, a turnip cutter, a roller, drills, and a blowing machine to take the hairiff out of wheat. Through the next thirty years the list of items on exhibition grew to about seven hundred and fifty, from over eighty exhibitors. Small implements were of course in the great majority, all at first produced from small workshops in towns and villages. Hoes, drills (including a corn drill by James Banks Stanhope of Revesby Abbey, 1852); cake crushers; chaff cutters (including one for horse or steam or hand, 1845); turnip scuffler (George

This plough was the common type on the Fen tract around the year 1800. The share was well steeled and sharpened with files, the wheel-coulter a sharpened steel wheel. Ploughmen would lay their heads low to aim by sighting between the two horses, and could make a furrow straight for hundreds of yards. To keep the horses apart they fixed a piece of wood pointed at both ends between them.

(General Review of Lincolnshire Agriculture, 1813)

Mawer of Horncastle, 1852); rollers, land roller, Cambridge roller, and a clod crusher or Cambridge roller (1855); the Earl Ducie invented a drag harrow or scarifier and cultivator which was several times exhibited. In 1862 a potato raiser, a machine for weighing cattle alive and a portable crane were offered.

By 1800 the use of animal power had not advanced much beyond the medieval, in spite of efforts with ploughs, a four-coultered plough, wheat and turnip drills, and hoe-ploughs. By mid-century inventiveness had transformed what man and beast could do. The plough, so old in concept, was made in improved form, as by Jno. Cooke & Co. of Lincoln from 1857, first shown in 1858. Before long he sold 2,000 in one year, but in 1865 he still had wood ploughs in his range. Hornsby offered his first plough in 1859. At once it took a leading place, being strong, light, adjustable, dirt-free, and especially controllable. Reapers — not generally successful — devised in 1822 and 1831 were followed by McCormick in 1831 and Hussey in 1833. The self-raking reaper was invented in 1852. Hussey's American Reaper appeared at the show that year, McCormick's Sheaf Delivery Reaper in 1863. The previous year John Wyatt Day, of Wootton, exhibited his mowing and reaping machine. Hornsby's reaper was delayed on rail in 1864, but its trial was allowed. He was, however, criticised for having one reaper on the stand at Gainsborough, and another at the trial at Gate Burton. (There were sometimes such double locations, as Boston/Eastville, and Market Rasen/Linwood, with a railway shuttle service between them). In 1865 there was the Hussey two-horse reaper, also a Samuelson and Ransome machine.

Inventive joiners and blacksmiths developed thrashing machines. They came into the age where the chief methods were flailing by hand or treading by animals. At the fourth show in 1840 at Horncastle was the first showing of portable thrashers, of Richard Hornsby and W. Hunter, and a non-portable by W. Grounsell. Four years later James Hart of Brigg showed a steam-driven thrashing machine. In 1845 Thos. Moor of Hayton, Notts., showed one, the next year a thrasher for two horses came from Barrett & Ashton of Hull.

Thomas Tupholme of Horncastle exhibited a steam engine and thrashing plant separately in 1847. The 1848 show saw the last of a thrashing machine to be powered by horses, by J. C. Grant of York.

The Society shows were a market place for these developments. Manufacture was being taken by the factories, by Richard Hornsby (in the agricultural market from 1840), Robey & Scott (1855), Foster (1857), Ruston Proctor (1858), all of Lincoln, and Marshall of Gainsborough (1848). Robey combined thrashing, straw shaking, riddling and winnowing, and in 1865 a double blast thrasher. James Coultas of Grantham pioneered the combined grain and fertiliser distributor in an extensive range which won R.A.S.E. prizes. He manufactured many types of cultivators and drills. His machinery included portable engines. Some eight others did not survive. By now the Rev. E. M. Chapman was able to urge that labourers ought not be regarded as combines nor mere machines.

The year 1854 saw the Royal Show at Lincoln, a successful one with attendance of 38,000. The N.L.A.S. held the servants and labourers classes at the Caistor ploughing meeting. The fact that the Society received no revenue of any note that year did not cause concern. The very next year the Royal Show also had some influence, even though it was as far away as Carlisle the local date was changed to avoid a clash.

Stockbreeding at this period

It is one thing to know or feel what is wanted in a situation, but without the appropriate resources not a great deal can be achieved. The early breeders knew by experiment and experience the value of crosses for their aims, which led to the importance of recording, and to Herd books being established. They knew that feeding had major influence, but were without the scientifically produced products to develop much. Competition did excite improvement. What they knew they tried to do better, the simpler things like the routine of feeding and exercise. Appearance will always be important,

Horse power for reaping with an implement of R. Hornsby & Sons Ltd. — one of the more aggressive companies of the agricultural revolution.

(Mr R. Hooley)

particularly alongside others, but then it was the main possibility of making a quality judgment. Their thinking was the foundation for future acceptance of better nutrition arising from the work of plant breeders and analysts, fertiliser manufacturers, and the implements and machinery to grow and handle it all. Flower, the yearling heifer at Horncastle in 1844 which won first prize and the sweepstake, also won as a three year old in 1846. It was size and weight which mattered then. At 1 year 4 months Flower weighed over half a ton.

Steam for the farm

Initiative in the locality followed the example of the successful use of steam in drainage pumping and on early railways by designing and building steam engines for farmers. Portable and non-portable engines appeared, the surviving companies being Richard Hornsby of Grantham, Clayton &

Shuttleworth, Ruston-Proctor, Robey & Scott, William Foster, Clayton & Co., all of Lincoln, and Marshall of Gainsborough. None of these, however, produced the earliest exhibits. James Hart of Brigg was first in 1844 with a static engine, Josh Thackrey of Doncaster second in 1845 with a 4 hp portable. Shimiels of Market Rasen in 1846 had a 2 hp portable, "the waste steam of which to cook potatoes, steam chaff, and for creeing linseed, barley, etc.". There were some minor exhibitors thereafter, notably Furley of Gainsborough, and Howden and Tuxford, both of Boston, but they did not affect the trend to the main manufacturers. Howden had, however, produced his first by 1839, Tuxford by 1842.

These engines were from 1½ to 12 horsepower. Their usage was as stationary engines for mills, and later for thrashers. Their portability referred to being moved on their wheels by horses. By 1851 Richard Hornsby had exhibited a dynamometer for testing the merits of steam engines. As to awards of premiums, the judging engineer from Belper complained in 1856 of the peculiar circumstances of the show: "The greatest part being entered by the makers as not for competition". Trying to do his duty, he praised the Robey & Scott 7 hp engine for its workmanship, strength, general arrangement, and work under trial. He drew attention to fuel consumption probably being more economical in regular work, and discounted this test — because in his experience some other engines were made especially for competition.

Two further tasks remained for steam power — traction, and the requirement to draw a plough. B. D. Taplin (a medical practitioner) of Lincoln was first, in 1861, with an 8 hp traction engine, invented and made by his company. It was priced at £275, about fifty pounds more than a portable. It was much like the present familiar pattern, except in reverse — the large driving wheels were in front. Two years later it was followed by Tuxford's Patent Road Locomotive or Traction Engine, again eight horsepower, but "working up to 16 hp" (but it used half as much coal again as a Hornsby). Then, from Kirton-in-Lindsey came the double development of traction and ploughing. Even so, none of the main later manufacturers appeared with traction engines at the shows of this Society.

Steam ploughing

The first premium for a System of Steam Cultivation was introduced in 1863 at the Boston Show. It seems to prove the effectiveness of such an initiative, but it was thirteen years after Lord Willoughby de Eresby had demonstrated steam ploughing at Edenham. (And near the end of the century Sir John Thorold thought that steam cultivation in many cases did a great deal of harm to strong land; that it was useful at times, but broke down ridge and furrow, and broke underdraining.)

There were four entries:

Amies & Barford of Peterborough offered the J. Fowler Apparatus for Steam Ploughing and Cultivating, for £295.

William Mawer of Stickney offered his own manufacture of the Smith Cultivator and Tackle, for an 8 hp steam engine, for £200. (In fact he had wanted to withdraw if the Fowler was to be there.)

John Henry Seels of Wainfleet showed a Cultivator and Harrow at £180, again for a steam engine. A Smith-Woolston invention, manufactured in Louth.

The award was won by Richardson & Darley of Kirton-in-Lindsey, with their Steam Traction Engine and Fowler's patent Anchor, Windlass, Steam Cultivating and Ploughing Tackle, complete, £800.

The ploughing offered was with one traction engine, and the cultivator being moved on steel rope traversing anchored pulleys. Fowler gave it more thought, and later paired more powerful engines. (His steam land draining machinery was not shown here.)

While the Annual Show had for years started on the last Wednesday in July, in 1864 the N.L.A.S. President, the Earl of Yarborough, asked for alteration so that Goodwood Week could be avoided. They would try, but it might result in great difficulty. In due course they regretted that they could not change; the date avoided the Royal Society's Show, and exhibitors passed on to the Yorkshire Show. Indeed they thought Goodwood was not regular, but the Cup Day there

31

THE FOUNDRY COMPANY.

ENGINEERS, MILLWRIGHTS,

IRON & BRASS FOUNDERS,

BOILER MAKERS, &c.,

MARKET RASEN, LINCOLNSHIRE.

VICTORIA IRON WORKS,

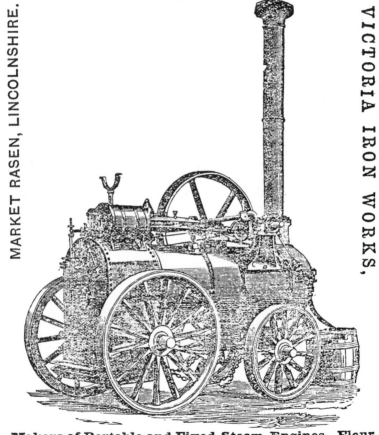

Makers of Portable and Fixed Steam Engines, Flour Mills, Cake Breakers, Cut Boxes, Circular Saw Tables, Cambridge and Flat Rolls, Tile Machines, Clay Mills, and Agricultural Implements of all kinds.

being Thursday, perhaps it would help if the N.L.A.S. made their principal day the Friday instead of Wednesday, for his Lordship's attendance. Later they were asked to reconsider but had to confirm their decision. The same answer went to G. F. Heneage, Esq. (With their descendants the same conflict often arises today concerning Ascot Week.) Later, Goodwood prevented H. Chaplin from acceding to be Vice Chairman.

Several letters were despatched in 1866 seeking the honour of the membership of a number of country gentlemen. The subscription was ten shillings for an annual member, or ten pounds in one sum for life. The Hon. Secretary did not demur twenty days later in reminding the Honble the Champion Dymoke for a reply. Sir Henry Dymoke responded in his own time with three guineas.

Cattle plague caused postponement of the N.L.A.S. 1866 Exhibition; to have been at Barton-on-Humber, until the next year, though the Servants and Labourers premiums were given as usual. The plague was Rinderpest, referred to as "the new pest"; not anthrax, which had been known for centuries. The chain of authority (it was before there were elected Councils) was firstly through the Magistrates, whom it was desired to meet to discuss measures to stay progress of the disease. The Lord Lieutenant, Lord Aveland, of Normanton Park, Rutland, was approached; a letter was addressed to the Privy Council, which was the route of recommendations to Government. Copies of Orders in Council on the subject were requested. A petition was sent to both Houses of Parliament. There was communication with the Cattle Plague Conference in London. The Member of Parliament was approached for support. The original warning of the onslaught had come to the N.L.A.S. from their President, the Earl of Yarborough, in a letter from Ireland in August the previous year. "More stringent measures against importation of stock from foreign countries" was the principal need. Insurance against losses was required.

Opposite: An advertisement of 1861 for one of the small companies which supplied so much early steam technology.

(Lincolnshire Archives)

Review as at 1867

In the thirty years' life of the North Lincolnshire Agricultural Society entries at their Shows were constantly buoyant, but increased unevenly in the categories. From 1845, the Society by then being well established, Servants and Labourers multiplied by over four, Implements by over eight, but Stock by only two.

While medicinal treatments for stock did develop, it cannot be said that there was much faith in the various concoctions. In the earlier days (1840) it was a general committee view that it was "well known that the great majority of those individuals who practise on diseases are perfectly void of science and consequently imperfectly qualified to administer remedies. There was some proper education for diseases of the horse, why not for beasts and sheep?" (The disparity arose because treatment of animals started with farriers.)

They offered a liberal premium for an essay on red water or rot and scour among sheep, and the downfall or black leg in cattle. This desire was urged in the context that then "under the blessing of Providence they would be enabled to supply abundance and satisfy the demands of the population and fill the dwellings of the poor with plenty". An essay on red water won the premium, but they would not circulate it. Six copies were made available for members.

A veterinary surgeon was appointed for the stock at the Show in 1864. The subject developed: In 1865 came J. G. Dickinson of Boston with his Dipping Mixture, and Ointment to destroy tick. In 1867 Day & Sons of Crewe exhibited Oils, black drinks, Cow drenches, Horse powders, and Horse, Cattle and Sheep Medicines. There was also, on a stand along with implements, Professor Tuson's Vegeto-Arsenical Dip.

There was no doubt of the ability of the Society to serve the needs of the agricultural community in its various aspects. In 1839 "the Gentlemen and Yeomanry of Louth and neighbourhood desired to subscribe and support — they had been diligent not only at a meeting but afterwards in the Market Place". Sometimes there was progress, "but not consistent with the wealth and importance of the district".

The dinner after a Show at the Town and Port of Gainsborough was in the ancient Town Hall, formerly the residence of the Lords of the Manor. "History could never record a larger number of guests around its tables, nor a company composed of the Lords of Manors, Gentlemen, Merchants, Farmers and Yeomanry . . . forwarding the patriotic objects of the North Lincolnshire Agricultural Society." In their Annual Reports the praise is constant, but they "did not conceive it arrogant. No Societies had shown greater energy or more marked results". However, reality was not lost — it was necessary "to produce a surplus, which was one of the strongest bonds of union". Or was reality lost when, in 1847 — close to the above — it was said that "they were the largest and most influential body of Agriculturists in the British Empire". It was when Lord Yarborough had died, and his son was being voted in to be the second President.

By 1867 the Secretary, Mr Hett, was getting less active, and an October meeting in Louth at 11 a.m. would mean a too early departure from, and a too late return to Brigg. For the succeeding short period he handed over to his son, Roslin. Administration had been firmly conducted, in a time when communication was hand written, if it was not by word of mouth. Situated in Brigg, the Secretary "was not aware whether there was a ploughing society in Lincoln or not". If the background of organisation changed, sometimes people just had to find out, as for example when the leading railway companies (1867) decided not to continue any special facilities, except for the Royal Show. It was nicely explained in reply to an objection to a member of Council that "no inefficient man can be forced on the Society, nor any inefficient man remain" — it was "in the hands of the members". It was once necessary to inform a competitor that his stock could achieve the 7.18 p.m. train from Louth for Barton, from where it would cross the Humber that night — by cattle boat and steam tug.

Rules and detail could be said to be partly formed by cases — for a labourer's child to have had school fees paid by a Board of Guardians was not considered as parochial relief — for a labourer not baptised, his father's entry in his Book was accepted for his age — for the thoroughbred stallion "Sir Richard" which was believed not thoroughbred, it was asked if the owner proposed to prove it — and the dark bay filly, by Maroon, was thought to be 4 years not 3 years old — having been noticed at the R.A.S.E. at Chester. Bulls had to have served cows in this County. As to Horticulture, a Band of Music in their tent would be "not at all objectionable".

Farming needs were comprehensively represented at the shows throughout this period, but in the case of much on exhibition it was groping without any real facility of research. But answers to problems were attempted, even as they are today with more accuracy but still some dangers. In the early shows there was a machine for making drainage tiles; there was wire netting; from the beginning of 1837 seed samples had been offered. Domestic items were comprehensive. The Stock competitions had led constantly to their improvement interlinked as it must have been with production of better fodder. "Something of everything" would be the summing up of what was made available for farmers, but not necessarily enough for their complete assessment; the Secretary wrote in 1854 to the Society of Arts in London that "to obtain the wools of Lincolnshire for their museum they should go to the Royal Show, because some of the principal breeders never exhibit with us". Machinery testing had diminished by 1865, with only reapers being tried.

The South Lincolnshire Agricultural Association, 1868 (Grantham/Sleaford)

There were societies in Sleaford and Grantham having purely local objectives. Committees appointed by them met on Monday, 20th January 1868, to form a new Society. Henry Chaplin, Esq. was in the chair. It was to be called The South Lincolnshire Agricultural Association. It had the objects of an annual meeting for the exhibition of stock, implements, etc., and the general promotion of Agriculture.

Clearly it was to be a Society using the northern one as an example, because it was further resolved that: Such meeting shall be held successively in different parts of South Lincolnshire. They started with Earl Brownlow as Patron, and Vice-Presidents such as the Duke of Rutland, Marquis of Exeter, Marquis of Bristol. Earl de Grey and Ripon. The second Lord Aveland (later the Earl of Ancaster), Lord Kesteven, Sir M. J. Cholmeley, Bt., M.P., Sir Thomas Whichcote, Bt., Sir John Thorold, M.P., Sir G. E. Welby-Gregory, Col. F. Fane, Col. J. Reeve, H. Chaplin, G. K. Jarvis and C. Thorold. The committee was geographically widespread in their area.

The first general meeting was at Sleaford Corn Exchange on the 2nd March. The first exhibition was arranged for 24th July at Grantham. Ladies were invited to the Public Dinner after. Implement prizes were for ploughs, cultivator, drag, harrows, drills, water drill, waggon, cart, horse hoe, dressing machine, corn blower, corn crusher, cake breaker, turnip cutter, root pulper, washing machine, churn, harness. It combined the South Lincolnshire Poultry Show. "Squire" Chaplin himself was a hunter judge.

While it was not unsuccessful the single-minded motivation of the northern society seemed to be absent. Indeed, some who might properly have been members in the area were linked with the northern society, as the Marfleets of Boothby Graffoe. The Mayor of Boston had given a prize for the show, something to show goodwill, though they had been suitably served by the north society. Lincoln was out of the Society orbit. The choices for moving the Exhibition around were too few. The Association lasted just under a twelve-month.

The breeds of Lincolnshire – pages 38 to 41

The Lincolnshire Shire Horse. This county is the ancestral home of the English Shire. Descended from Flemish and Frisian heavy horses brought over in the sixteenth century for fen drainage work, they grew larger and particularly strong. They came to be bred over too great an area for the Lincolnshire name to hold, but nevertheless the great Fen Blacks are traceable as the ancestry of all modern pedigree Shires. The illustration of 1907 shows "Hitchin Magnet" of Mr Welch of Rauceby.

(J. W. Ruddock & Sons Ltd)

President of the Society Mr C. L. Bembridge in 1980 with the Supreme Champion Lincoln Red, his Anwick Hannah 340th; also showing his daughter Mrs S. A. Richardson, farm foreman Mr Ted White, and herdsman Mr John Cook.

(Lincolnshire Echo)

Early in this century nine out of ten cattle in the county were Lincoln Red Shorthorns. Breeders' private records led to the establishment of the Herd Book in 1895. Following new Ministry of Agriculture standards, from 1946 beef and dairy cattle were divided into separate breeding considerations. The breed's favour now is based on the rate of early live-weight gain. The present polled strain was developed in the 1940s.

Mr Andrew Read and Mr Robert Watts hold Lincoln Longwools to be judged by Mr G. H. Smith.

(Lincolnshire Echo)

40

Lincolnshire Curly Coated Pig. This old local breed was increasing in numbers some eighty years ago, when the Large White was predominant in the county. The Curly Coat was large, and never outstandingly popular. While it has recently become extinct, the Chester White, bred in the U.S.A. and now being imported, is in part derived from it.

(Kenneth Oldroyd, FRPS)

The Lincolnshire Buff Hen. The name became attached to a breed started in the county in 1853 as a cross between the Shanghai (colloquially "the Cochin") and the White Dorking. They became extremely popular. They were large birds, perhaps too large, because some forty years later they were being cross-bred further. After a period of confusion, and some misrepresentation as to which was which, the breed appears to have devolved into the Buff Orpington.

(Lincolnshire College of Agriculture)

41

The amalgamated Society adopted the certificate of the former North Lincolnshire Agricultural Society. The above was awarded at the 1869 Show to Joseph Ward of Hemswell, with six pounds, for having been a servant in husbandry with Mr John Coupland for fifty-seven years.

(Lincolnshire Museums)

The Lincolnshire Agricultural Society

A strong feeling had developed throughout Lincolnshire that the North Lincolnshire Agricultural Society and the South Lincolnshire Agricultural Association should amalgamate. It seemed that combined action in promoting their purposes would be desirable. There was "much yet to be achieved" and the ambition was "to be one of the foremost Societies in Great Britain".

From minutes of other meetings it is apparent that there would be duplication of work in this one County for trials of the increasing range of machinery on offer; and it is possible that the calendar for Shows was getting tight. There was much competition from neighbouring Counties on the south. Some of the locations in the north were small for the increasing size, and therefore cost, of larger shows. There was also a catalyst for the change. Another Reform Bill had divided Lincolnshire into three constituencies instead of the two from 1832. It had operated for the first time in the 1868 General Election. To have one Society, the new Lincolnshire Agricultural Society — the present one — was a fundamental break in the localised structure of living. The North and the South Societies had been co-terminus with the form of local — very local — government. It was all based on and stemming from the same people in their social intercommunication. (Mr Walter Dudding's proposition in 1878 was lost: that no politics be discussed apart from agricultural interests.)

A mid-Lincolnshire constituency had intervened, leading to references to "the three divisions". This situation was met by having one overall Society. That ultimate decision, in the end unanimous, was not reached without contrary vigorous expressions of opinion. At the first Annual General Meeting on the 29th October 1869, it was stated that it was the "duty of every member never to allude to, and to forget as much as possible events of the past". Also it was reported that "more than apparent difficulties surrounded the proceedings which led to the amalgamation". Geo. Tomline, Esq. of Riby Grove for one had resigned in anticipation of the merger. Complaint came that the County Gentlemen had not been consulted. Secretary Mr Hett's opinion on that was that it was not a new Society, and what those Gentlemen who did not subscribe to either of the existing Societies had to do with the amalgamation of them he did not see. He fancied they would have been astonished at being consulted. He also stated that Yorkshire landed gentry gave more support to their Society than was the case in North Lincolnshire. (This last remark appears to discount their greater numbers and the better focus of their County Town.) The opposition in the South Society, feared by their secretary, had come to naught.

While some could (and still can) urge that North and South Lincolnshire were like different counties, the amalgamation had been done "on fair and friendly terms". The two committees had met at the Corn Exchange in Lincoln, General Meetings had been held, negotiating committees formed:

The North Lincolnshire Agricultural Society
Hon. A. L. Melville, William Garfit, Esq., William Hutton, Esq., Edwd. Heneage, Esq., M.P. (Proposer), Mr William Torr, Mr C. M. Nainby, Mr Thomas Randell (Seconder), Major Grantham, Mr John Iles, Mr James Martin, Mr Geo. Cartwright

The South Lincolnshire Agricultural Association
W. E. Welby, Esq., M.P., Sir Jno Thorold Bt., M.P., Colonel F. Fane, Henry Chaplin, Esq. (Proposer), J. Hardy, Esq. (Seconder), Mr B. Tomlinson, Mr R. G. F. Howard, Mr J. H. Casswell, Mr C. Beasley, Mr W. Marriott, Mr C. Clarke

By the end of November 1868 their joint proposals had been ratified by separate general meetings of the two societies at Market Rasen and Sleaford; details to be arranged by the secretaries at Lincoln in December. Lord Yarborough was asked for his hearty support for its influence upon others, and he was made Life President. The first General Meeting of this Lincolnshire Agricultural Society was at the Corn Exchange in Lincoln on the 8th January 1869, with William Hutton, Esq. in the chair. The proposals were adopted. Thus the new L.A.S. was now in being. That is the foundation date. "The first object of the society shall be to promote improvement in every branch of rural economy, and the industry, providence, and welfare of the labouring classes by distributing premiums, and by other means best calculated to accomplish such ends." All prizes were to be open to competition of the whole of the United Kingdom, except for Labourers and Servants, who had to be of Lincolnshire.

The business concerning officers and rules was accompanied by certain direct resolutions:

"The Lord Lieutenant of the County to be the patron" — the words 'if willing' were later added to this first peremptory statement.

"The exhibition to alternate between North and South Lincolnshire, and Lincoln shall be neutral" — meaning that a Lincoln show shall not upset the alternations.

Earl Brownlow was requested by letter to be the Patron; Henry Chaplin, Esq. — the famous squire of Blankney — now aged 28 — the Chairman. The Vice-Presidents list included the Earl of Scarbrough, Colonel Amcotts, M.P., Col. F. Fane, Edward Heneage, Esq., Henry Thorold, Esq., T. J. Dixon, Esq. Some eminent persons refused, notably the more distant ones.

On 5th February 1869 a secretary was appointed at a meeting of the Council. He had to reside at Lincoln, his salary to be £100 a year plus expenses; additionally £5 per cent of general subscription and donation income. The latter he had to collect at Markets at his own expense, and most of these were by now directly accessible by railway from Lincoln: Boston,

Horncastle, Grimsby, Market Rasen, Grantham, Barton-on-Humber, Gainsborough, Spalding. Spilsby had just got its branch line, but for some years it would be a journey via Boston or Grimsby, as were Alford and Louth. Similarly, posting from Essendine may have been quicker for Stamford and Bourne, and from Algarkirk for Long Sutton.

As well as discussing the Lincoln Show, the Council voted for a dinner after each meeting at the expense of the Society, at a cost not to exceed seven shillings each. This ignored the previous secretary's well known opinion that far too much eating and drinking took place. He was presented with plate costing £50. The Society was in good order; the funds of the N.L.A.S. had contributed £1,799.6.4., the S.L.A.A. £500. 1054 members were inherited from the two societies. As an organisation it dates back to the founding of the N.L.A.S. on 13th October 1836; through the same active families it is connected with the Lincoln Society from 21st April 1819. Families, notably the Earls of Yarborough, connect it with the Lindsey Society which began on 16th April 1799.

The first Show of the present society, 1869

The council proceeded to the organisation of the 1869 Lincoln Show, to be on 29th, 30th and 31st July. It was designated as the first. There was no need for a humble and cautious beginning, because the connection with potential exhibitors was established through thirty-two years. The N.L.A.S. was able to go to Lincoln anyway, which it had already done. They followed the previous type of arrangements, at the same time setting the pattern for many future years. The President, Vice-President, and Lincoln Corporation began the prize list — with awards relative to horses. The City offered the Guildhall for a meeting to collect donations for the Show (it came to £144.13.6.), and for Society

Opposite: The title page of the catalogue of the first Exhibition of the present Society. It makes no concession to its forebears.

(Lincolnshire Archives)

LINCOLNSHIRE
AGRICULTURAL SOCIETY.

Patron:

The Right Hon. The EARL BROWNLOW, Lord Lieutenant of the County.

President:

The Right Hon. The EARL of YARBOROUGH.

Chairman for the Year: HENRY CHAPLIN, Esq., M.P.

A

CATALOGUE OF THE ENTRIES

OF

Poultry, Pigeons, Seeds & Roots,

AGRICULTURAL IMPLEMENTS,

And Miscellaneous Articles,

FOR THE PRIZES OFFERED AT THE

FIRST EXHIBITION

OF THE SOCIETY,

HELD AT LINCOLN,

On Thursday, Friday, and Saturday, July 29, 30, & 31, 1869.

Honorary Director:

Mr. WILLIAM TORR, Aylesby Manor, Grimsby.

Stewards:

Mr. JOHN DAVY, Owersby, Market Rasen.
MAJOR GRANTHAM, West Keal Hall, Spilsby.
Mr. JAMES HORNSBY, Castlegate House, Grantham.

Mr. R. G. F. HOWARD, Temple Bruer, Lincoln.
  ,, JAMES MARTIN, Wainfleet, Boston.
  ,, WILLIAM PARKE, Stragglethorpe, Newark.
  ,, ROBERT WYLES, Little Ponton, Grantham.

Stewards of Finance:

EDWARD HENEAGE, Esq., Hainton Hall, Wragby: *Chairman.*

Mr. CHARLES CLARKE. Scopwick. Sleaford.
  ,, JAMES MARTIN, Wainfleet, Boston.

Mr. BRUCE TOMLINSON, Asgarby, Sleaford.
  ,, WILLIAM TORR, Aylesby Manor, Grimsby.

Auctioneers:

Mr. WILLIAM MAWER & Mr T. B. RICHARDSON, Lincoln.

Secretary:

Mr. STEPHEN UPTON, St. Benedict's Square, Lincoln.

Council Meetings. They also offered the land, thirty-three acres of common east of the City, known as the Cowpaddle. It was divided by the recent railway to Grantham, but a temporary footbridge could be constructed, as could sidings for direct delivery of machinery and supplies. A level crossing and one siding were achieved. The offer was all in the mould of town and country life being dependent on each other; horses, cattle and sheep were common in the streets, and farm women with their produce. A local committee was formed for liaison with the host town.

Thrashing machines would be at work at the show, driven by portable steam engines. These and all implements would be moved by horse or manpower. There were to be trials for Crushing Mills, Corn Screens, Root Pulpers, Turnip Cutters, and Cake Breakers. The Manchester Sheffield & Lincolnshire Railway would run a special train for stock and implements from Manchester.

Continuing the affairs of shows of the former societies the council decided on some rule revisions — more prizes for drivers of steam engines because of equal merit for the second prize — an appeal from Mr O'Grady about his game fowl having been disqualified in 1868 (for the last N.L.A.S. Show) was met with no retraction and no apology — certain horse classes were now to be ridden before the judges. Certificates were to be similar to those of the former N.L.A.S. The Council Dinner cost three shillings a head, with malt liquor and waiters, but not wine.

It was the first show of a Society for which the whole of Lincolnshire was now open to them. In 1870 the office was moved to St. Benedict Square in Lincoln. The papers were sent from Brigg on the 3.30 train. It did result, however, in the abandonment of the smaller centres in the north. There had already been doubt by Mr John Hett, the N.L.A.S. secretary, about Barton as a venue for 1867, but "they were persuaded by an imposing list of names". It had turned out average, and satisfactory.

As well as the all-county membership, for the 1869 show a feature of the S.L.A.A. show at Grantham was incorporated —

the Poultry Show — Dorkings, Game, Spanish, Brahmas, Cochins, Hamburghs, Bantams, Polands, French. Also Geese, Ducks, Turkeys and Pigeons.

There were representative exhibits of every branch of farming needs, in of course the developed patterns of the day. Portable and stationary steam engines were now an established form of power — with still an 8 hp portable made locally by the Foundry Company of Market Rasen. One inventor showed a competitive idea — a horse powered machine with a strong flywheel.

Thrashing machines took their usual place; the rollers as invented by Cambridge, and water-ballast ones; grinding mills, metal and stone; carts, sporting, pony, light general purpose, Norwich, Whitechapel (a pony and a dog cart respectively). There were newly invented nailless horse shoes, the self-acting hydraulic ram to raise 1000-5000 gallons a day, hurdles for oxen and other animals; and for their ailments medicine chests, complete. A large part of the variety of things for sale was now being offered by local agents. They took the opportunity of the peripatetic Show to exhibit at their own towns. Velocipedes were there, garden tables, guns by Hanson of Lincoln. Alongside each other were the French and the Persian iron bedsteads. Exhibitors came from as far away as Warrington, Essex, and Northampton.

The judges were very busy in those three days. The prize list for people had by now come to include Foremen, Shepherds, Labourers, Head Waggoners (so long as they had a character for sobriety or "did not return drunk with their horses"), Male Servants in husbandry, Drivers of steam engines. Also, for long service: Blacksmiths, Carpenters, Female Servants. Horse & Stock competition was for agricultural horses, hunters and roadsters; short-horned cattle; the cottager's milch cow and heifer; pigs. The sheep were divided between Longwools, and Leicesters, and hog wool fleeces of Ewe or Wether wool.

The Farmers' Magazine criticised the "chaos that reigned at Lincoln". This was based mostly on the "spinning out" of the horse classes over two days, resulting in: "nothing worthwhile the second day. The Lincolnshire Agricultural Society must have the resources and purse like that of Croesus, judging by the way everything is done". They also complained that catalogues were late by an hour, horses in the sheds were not visible to the public, prize award labels were distributed too slowly, and snacks cost too much relative to the price of the dinner.

It had, however, been a comprehensive affair. Two rings, 200 sheep and 50 pig pens, 80 cattle and 20 bull stalls, 120 horse boxes and stabling for a further 200. There were 30 dog boxes, and the dog show stand alone had seating for 600. With lunch rooms, committee rooms, and — an innovation — ladies cloakrooms, it had all cost half the society's resources, over one thousand pounds.

The Society established

There was cheer and euphoria at the October General Meeting: "There was no equal in extent or importance to the purely agricultural County of Lincolnshire. There were no tall chimneys except those connected with the making of agricultural implements, with feeding stuffs and fertilisers, or the grinding of corn". Thanks to the City of Lincoln for all its help and support. They had been anxious about the number of members but there were now 1,848, which was 794 more in the year. Praised were the well conducted, intelligent, and faithful servants, of whom 265 had competed. Extensions of this class and for drivers of steam engines were referred to. To promote the interest and welfare of the labouring classes by distributing prizes was one of the fundamental objects of the society.

Of the stock, there had been so few "overfed" shorthorns; "improved Lincolns" among the sheep were excellent in "lustre wool" and in "mutton for the millions". All was a credit. Hunters and Roadsters had been viewed from a well-filled stand. Lincolnshire pigs had taken most of the prizes. The new Eureka smut and separating machine for mills was most important. The railway facilities had been excellent.

Hounds from the most celebrated packs of the County had been much appreciated at the show.

Six hundred noblemen, ladies and gentlemen attended the dinner. The total funds stood at £3,062.5.1 It was an observation rather than a warning note, that the Royal Agricultural Society may have taken over the effectiveness of machinery trials, which in any case were expensive. Into all this a minor complaint was introduced about the right of a new member of Council, C. S. Fieldsend, but he was definitely entitled, having become a member of the new Society.

At this time the chairman, Henry Chaplin, Esq., owned 25,000 acres, with an income of £40,000 a year. His disposal of it was rapid, and he had to sell his estate twenty-eight years later. Some said he was over-indulgent as a landlord. The farm wage in Lindsey and Kesteven was 12s. to 15s. a week, perhaps 18s. Some had allotments, some had cows. It was considered nationally a good standard.

Before long a variation was put to a resolution, in that the Society area should include villages out of the County, up to fifteen miles from Grantham as in the old South Lincolnshire Agricultural Association. The proposition was only just lost, at 18 votes to 17. Two years later there was no mood to agree with the Norfolk Agricultural Association's suggestion to amalgamate into one General Eastern Counties Association of all the counties adjoining Norfolk. It was said that H.R.H. The Prince of Wales had propounded the idea. Six years later it came forward and was refused again. The Society was in a position of strength.

Marshall's of Gainsborough proved in part their worth by their medals, awarded at many exhibitions.

In May 1872 the Finance Committee was empowered to purchase engraved or lithographed portraits of the Patron, the President and the Chairman for each exhibition — to be hung in the Council Room.

The Annual Shows

The star attraction at the second show, at Sleaford in 1870, was Hermit, "Squire" Chaplin's famous 1867 Derby winner. Judged as the best hunter-stallion, it was remarked that it was "worth double the admission charge to gaze on". It was noted as the neatest, handsomest, best proportioned, good limbed muscular short-jointed horse entirely free from lumber ever seen. It also had a beautiful frame.

Stock was praised generally, though recorded comments on other horses did not all seem so: model of power, legs of iron, thick shoulder, good forehand, falls off behind with legs too far away, leggy as a fowl, going very oily, nice character, flash-looking, slow as a man in his gallop, peculiar-formed pasterns, knew how to use her hips. Shorthorns, a very pretty lot, were detailed as having blooming looks, wonderful barrel, pretty loin, better in frame than quality, sharp in her hair. The challenge cup award for the sheep was disagreed between three judges on each side. "The old game of pull devil pull baker was tried but neither party proved the stronger." An umpire was refused, so all departed without a decision. (It really seems they had had a small tug o'war.)

Several gentlemen got up and spoke at the dinner. Lord Kesteven averred that horses here were much better than those he had just seen at Oxford; and the riders there were not so good either. Out of twenty-one entries for the best cultivated farm (at Oxford) the winner had been a lady, a native of Lincolnshire. The Hon. A. L. Melville said that he had had great difficulty in explaining the landlord and tenant system to an American, who could not understand the putting of money into someone else's land. Mr Charles Bramley-Tennant replied that it was because of the encouragement of

Mr Pilkinton's prize-winning "capital team of roans" at Sleaford in 1870. Unfortunately there was no other entry in the class.
(Illustrated London News)

landlords, but Mr Torr went much further, suggesting that with good landlords and good labourers no leases were required. (In 1850 tenants of the Yarborough and the Chaplin estates expressed preference for the customs of the estates.)

Mr W. E. Welby M.P., the Chairman, praised the organisers of the Show for keeping one thing in mind, rare as that was, namely the promotion of the science of agriculture, and the welfare of all connected with it. They had allotted funds relative to labour, and to chemical analysis. He hoped that Show locations in small towns would not strain the finances.

The organisation of the Annual Show had achieved a pattern, to be steered by minor decisions. The starting point was to decide its location. In the first few years there was competition for it. In 1872 a deputation from Spalding guaranteed a local fund of £500, plus £150 for prizes, and a free military band. Boston offered unspecified generous terms, and was not chosen. Deputations from Lincoln, Grantham and Stamford for 1874 produced two decisions — firstly that the

Show should be in the south, secondly by 22 votes to 13 that it should be at Grantham. That town had made a specific offer; Stamford had played on the attractions of Burghley Park. The enthusiasm shown by Brigg in 1871 in decorating the town was not universal. It led, however, to long lasting arrangements for local subscribers of one pound or more being admitted free to the Show.

For 1875 there were deputations from Lincoln again, this time in competition with Grimsby and Louth. The arrangements at Grimsby had advanced too far when the Earl of Yarborough died for the Show to be postponed. The next year options were kept open, and the Lincoln Show was held where the Royal Show would have been — if it had come. The rotation round the County was maintained, competition or not, just as the N.L.A.S. had done. Though the town did not offer, in 1863 the N.L.A.S. had decided on Gainsborough for 1864: "the inhabitants would no doubt take steps to raise a local fund". Twenty years later the Secretary of the L.A.S. was to communicate with the Burgess Constable of Gainsborough and ascertain 'if it is the wish of the inhabitants for the exhibition to be at that town'. It was so held, but complaints ensued — too late — when it clashed with Market Day. It had been moved to avoid the dates of the Royal Show at York.

With road surfaces little different from the adjoining fields, no telephones, and steam the strongest motive power, organisation depended on the railway. The crispness of the administration has its surprises. The closing date for show entries was only three weeks before the opening day. It was firmly held, to the extent of a member resigning because his entry for a labourer was refused as a day late. Machinery from as far away as Plymouth was rejected because it might not arrive in time; another example was J. and F. Howard of Bedford whose steam ploughing apparatus could not be accommodated for lateness. Nor would they countenance the substitution of a grey for a bay horse.

For the transport of exhibits — machinery or stock — and people — the railways were approached early. Dealings included the Manchester, Sheffield & Lincolnshire, the

Midland, Great Northern, Great Eastern, the Trent, Ancholme & Grimsby, Lancashire & Yorkshire, North Eastern, North Staffordshire, Bristol & Exeter, London & North Western, and South Yorkshire Railway Companies. The first four, the most local ones, were the most helpful, but it was clear that for the location to be in the hands of one company was cautionary. If the Show was at Grimsby attempts were made to interest Continentals to come via the Steam Packets. The main concession was that if stock or implements did not sell, then the return journey would be free. The North Eastern did not agree to that; return charges were made, which in some cases could have been avoided by using another railway. For some show sites either sidings or a special unloading platform were built. The lack of proximity to the railway almost lost Louth the show, until the Borough promised to improve the road surface. The site was one mile from the station. Extra trains were run, sometimes at late hours. Reduced fares were usually one and a quarter for the return ticket. Important publicity was by bills on stations. Societies combined in order to negotiate better and more standard terms, with some general agreement in a Railway Clearing House circular of 1875. Just the next year the G.N.R. and the M.S. & L.R. gave transport to and from the show free.

The later nineteenth century

Development of the Society was far ahead of its predecessors, which had sought fundamental support from county gentlemen. It was now beyond their scope. (In 1873 there were one hundred and twenty-four resident owners of one thousand acres and upwards in the whole County. The non-resident owners comprised only a handful.) Subscribers increased with the diversity of the Shows, to include traders connected with agriculture, indeed also others who subscribed just to support the objects of the Society.

This is not to say, however, that support from the gentry was not still strong. The most Hon. the Marquess of Exeter,

George Nevile, Esq., and R. H. C. Nevile, Esq. became Vice-Presidents — the last resigning before long because his military duties took him away. Industrialists also, as Clayton, Ruston, Hornsby, and Shuttleworth, the last-named being retained though he had often to be away.

The success of each year depended on what affected farmers — diseases, weather, costs, prices. The Royal Commission on Rinderpest had adopted a "Stamping out" policy, and by 1867 it was thought to be exterminated. Pleuro-pneumonia and foot-and-mouth had been around for thirty years, and cattle plague regulations nearly got rid of them. An 1869 Act of Parliament regulated imports to some extent, but cattle plague broke out again in 1872, also in 1877 with cases in London and Hull. The attention of Clerks of Petty Sessions and Borough Authorities was drawn to the need to guard against its entry into Lincolnshire. It was Rinderpest again. The R.A.S.E. made recommendations, sent to every member. It was resolved that "nothing short of total prohibition of Foreign livestock will meet the exigencies of the case. This need not apply to dead meat. The consumer would not be affected". It was passed to Boroughs, M.P.s in the County, and to the Privy Council. Cattle markets and fairs were closed, the decision about the next two exhibitions was delayed. The restrictions, which applied to cattle, sheep and goats, lasted in Lincolnshire some weeks longer than in neighbouring counties, and the Society despatched a memorial to the Privy Council seeking their removal.

While the weather as a hazard, or support, is a constant factor in farming, to the two or three days of a Society's Show it assumes special importance. It was not always dry and sunny — in the rain the judges usually carried on, but the visitors did not arrive in full numbers. There was a mixture of factors at Stamford in 1893 — a good season but a wet week for the Show, and four others in competition. It took two-thirds of invested funds to meet the loss. For farmers most of the seventies had been bad seasons, to an acute position in 1879, when wheat at 15½ bushels to the acre was half the usual.

Prices had been buoyant in 1870/71, during the Franco-

Prussian war, but the major problem for all began in 1873 to 1874 when imports began to tell. Over a period it included butter and cheese and dead meat in addition to corn. Some tenants could not pay their rents. The area of wheat in the country fell to two-thirds that of 1859. Permanent pasture took its place.

With all this, the entrance receipts from 1879 to 1900 never exceeded the £1,754 of the opening show of 1869. They varied from £711 to £1,512. The local contributions increased considerably from the then expanding town of Lincoln, but not significantly from the other locations. In 1896 the Annual Membership was down to 912. A two-day show was tried in Gainsborough, but there was not much saving — the same standard buildings were required, and judging had to be got through in two days. But in 1897, Sleaford, with only five thousand inhabitants raised £700, and decorated the streets.

It was not unknown for the Society to need its reserves to pay its commitments, between years at profit. What must be considered as the basis of its sound continuance was the ever increasing entry of implements and machines. The word "improved" and "invented" are of constant occurrence. This was the market place for workshops large and small. It was not the only outlet for them — it was the Lincolnshire outlet. The larger factories had vast world wide connections, and some better known names were not regular at the Shows. By 1869 there were 84 reaping machines to test at the Manchester field trials. Hornsby was in the top five, then naming his machine the "Manchester Reaper".

The McCormick self-binding reaper of 1870 did not catch on until twine was enabled instead of the binding wire (shown in 1893). (The Appleby binder was ahead of them here, in 1880.) The 1877 cream separator was a great advance. Churns, butter driers, milk testers, refrigerators, heaters, cheese-making apparatus — there was little that could not and did not receive genuine improvement. In 1882 the implement entry was two hundred up on the previous year. Traction engines increased in number, 1886 seeing Burrell of Thetford, Robey of Lincoln, Marshall of Gainsborough, and R. Hornsby with his narrow gauge traction engine, which some thought very liable to overturn. John Fowler returned regularly with an 8 hp model, joined by Allchin of Northampton, Aveling & Porter, Ruston-Proctor, and Wm. Foster. There was the small manufacturer, Collitt of Boston, with a 5 hp machine. Their usage at Shows was limited to stop complaints about the smoke.

No sooner was the agricultural world linked with steam power at its zenith for operation and movement than oil and petroleum engines began to appear at the show. Richard Hornsby & Son showed their pioneering compression-ignition oil engine, the Hornsby-Akroyd Patent Safety Horizontal Oil Engine, 3½ and 4½ hp. The year 1892 also included a Robey and a Crossley gas engine, Blackstone vertical steam engines, portable engines, and further steam traction engines by Fowell of St. Ives, and a Wallis and Stevens, with its sloping boiler. Strangely, main manufacturers in the County — Ruston, Marshall, Foster, Clayton & Shuttleworth — were the latest to exhibit traction engines. Three large manufacturers from away appeared at the 1895 Exhibition. Richard Hornsby had a new two-speed 6 hp traction engine that year, but the period was really marked on the power side by more oil or petroleum stationary engines, for barn machinery — Bates & Co., Robey, Hett's patent "Accessible", Knight & Weyman and Clayton & Shuttleworth's patent, and Campbell.

Other assistance to farmers was represented, gradually increasing year by year. Dipping compositions, from Joseph Bentley; cake meal manures, seeds of William Sinclair; seeds from Sutton; Osmond's cattle oils and dips; manures of Cannon & Co., embrocation, pig powders, drenches, "Zozzinol" for scour and diarrhoea in all stock; calf food, horse and cattle spice; Battle, Maltby and Bower showed dips, disinfectants, powders, ointments, lamb drinks and Lincolnshire Embrocation; the Farmers Company had cakes and manures; there was a sterilising plant; Tomlinson & Hayward with dips and ointments, Pearson Bros. (now within B.O.C.M.) linseeds and oils — all represented scientific work and presaged its tremendous advance in the twentieth century. "Huskolein" would cure husk, hoose, host, or husk and

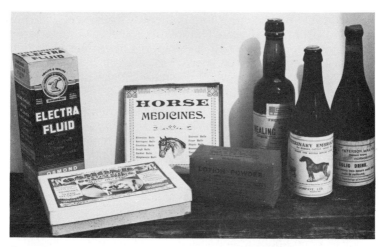

Remedies: Mixtures put together with superficial knowledge did good or harm or nothing. Private remedies were also concocted, even "to prevent a horse kicking up at the heels."　　　　　　　　　　(Lincolnshire Museums)

A Lincolnshire Wagon. Large, spindle sided, high and narrow. A first class harvest wagon that would nearly turn in its own length.
(Institute of Agricultural History and Museum of English Rural Life,
University of Reading)

tapeworms. Blacksmith's equipment, Insurance, driving garments from Zacharias of Oxford, all branches of farm needs were now represented. An Exhibition Car of the Canadian Pacific Railway Company showed samples of grain, grasses, fruits and minerals from Manitoba and British Columbia; their purpose was the seeking of immigrants.

Ladies were not forgotten, for there was Chemical Diamond Jewellery, a cement for repairing china and glass, and maybe for them the Bathing Tent. Perhaps the repair cement is doubtfully theirs — it would also fix leather on to billiard cues.

The organisation

There is no doubt about the depth of the depression which had started in 1872. Free trade, the railways in the New World, and steamers brought in the prairie corn in increasing quantities. Costs here were increased by the Education Act which removed boys from work, and the labour on farms was not used efficiently. With some poor harvests, there were farms without tenants, and rents had to be halved. Lord Ripon's land on the Heath at Nocton was down to 12s. an acre; cattle dropped from £14 to £8 a head. Industry, then so closely related to agriculture, became depressed, and from 1886 it had foreign tariffs to contend with. There was a slight improvement from 1880 to 1884, but it was the end of the century before recovery. There were some, as the Lord Monson, who thought Consols were a better, indeed certain, investment, rather than the varying yield of land. Part of his estate, North Carlton, was sold. (It was later re-purchased.)

In 1880 the Society was considering a further loss of £900 on the previous year. It was necessary to practise "economy in some details on hand to make expenditure correspond with current income". The annual financial results were affected by their judgment in the premiums they offered in the hope of entries, and by the amount raised for the wood of the stands and shedding after the Shows. Proper pricing of all activities had already included manning the gate turnstiles instead of letting them out to bidders. The turnstiles themselves had been introduced ("as used at the Crystal Palace") because people had crowded in uncontrollably. Better stabling had put up the cost. No premium, as in 1880 for Leicester sheep, meant no entries.

Steering their way, decisions were made on sites, local committees, and assessments of the previous year. In the summer of 1874 the Society of Arts wrote from London suggesting the founding of scholarships for their examinations in the Technology of Agriculture and Rural Economy. No steps could be taken "at present". If the Royal Show was to be in Lincoln in 1876 they would seek to merge the two shows. The city was most anxious to receive the R.A.S.E. A subscription fund was raised and in the event £1,000 was sent from that. It did not come and the Lincolnshire Exhibition was held as usual.

In 1882 the death of the Hon. A. L. Melville was much regretted — "scarcely absent from meetings, always advocated their interests" he had been a Vice-President of the N.L.A.S. and the present Society from the beginning.

Prizes and entries varied upon the basic pattern, and a few disputes were resolved each year. Oxen, and pairs of oxen, were still in the prize list in 1874. Shoeing Smiths and Labourers classes were varied and increased in 1877, a result of the Society's suggestion book. The next year Colonel Fane offered a new prize to farmers' sons as engine drivers and stokers. A special prize for a fleece of wool from a three-year Lincolnshire Ram was put forward; the sheep exhibition was strengthened by new prizes from Bass, Ratcliff & Gretton in 1886; the Burton & Lincoln Brewery was more direct: it offered samples of Ales, Stout, and Scotch Whisky. The same year brought in Bee Driving, which was driving bees from a straw hive, and capturing the Queen; also explaining the method and object. For the first time, 1889, there was a prize for a group of four Hunting Colts, or fillies, and similarly for Shires, by the same sire. The shoeing competitions over the years had led to a marked improvement in skill and quality.

Visitors were attracted by the driving and the jumping, and they showed great interest in the honey and appliances, though these classes themselves were not thought to bring the support they deserved. The implements were always an attraction. Evening extensions were tried, with a band from the locality — as the Louth Artillery — but were only occasionally satisfactory. Parades of cattle, of agricultural horses, of hunters, of hackneys, harness horses, and a military band were the general constituents of the days' programmes. The public lunches were well supported. Indeed, it proved impossible to limit toasts to a suggested five; The Queen, Prince of Wales and Royal Family; the Society; Mayor and the local town; and the Chairman. The very idea was dropped.

For some years the Society had had a Suggestion Book available to members. It was examined regularly by the Council. Bees and beekeeping exhibits were a result of it; short-woollen sheep were noted for consideration as a class; the idea of an exhibition of the improved methods of butter-making was referred for a report on its cost. For this last item the Lindsey County Council gave a prize, but withdrew it in 1901, which reduced the entries.

Miss Bloomer was asked to return the money paid to her so that Lady Pigot should have it, because Victoria Victrix had had a calf on the 10th September, so she was indisputably a cow, Champion, class 6. A three year Gelding lost its award because it was not a thoroughbred. A stoker was disqualified because he was found to have coal on his person. By contrast, a member returned an award when he found his brood mare to be barren.

During this period of the depression there still appears to have been adequate scope for the production of the shows, given care and economy. The number of entries overall was reasonably constant — the worst year was 1881 when it was 852. In 1869 it had been 998. It was to be the Show of 1897, perhaps with better times in view, when it climbed up by about 200 to 1319. The main source of revenue, the implement makers and agents, continued their strong support. Cattle, Sheep, and the beekeepers increased in numbers. Engine drivers' last year was 1892, Shoeing Smiths 1893, even though that year the entry was "large and keen". They had both been intermittent for ten years. Wool had become steady after years with no entries. Servants and Labourers were down a little.

Absolutely dependent upon the railways as they were, it was helpful in 1888 to be informed that six railway companies, including the four local ones, were now constructing a special type of vehicle for the faster conveyance of Stock by passenger train. It was not in the same vein in 1899 when the companies suddenly refused to put the Society notices up at their stations, which happened after they had undertaken to do so, and after they had been printed.

Outside considerations

The general opinion of the Society members was evident on occasions — for example they were not against free trade and open competition with producers in all parts of the world (1878). The same year the Council strongly approved the establishment of a stud book for Cart Horses, as propounded by the English Cart Horse Association. The opening of the new Corn Exchange in Lincoln was well received in 1880, superseding the one of 1848. Before then the merchants and farmers had met in the open on Cornhill. Brayford Pool was then the centre of commerce, corn being shipped in great quantities, from the Eastern Wharf.

They and their predecessors took action towards the authorities when animal diseases had been prevalent. In 1884 it concerned foot-and-mouth. Again importation was blamed as the cause. "Grievous losses had fallen on an industry already burdened by disadvantages."

There was negotiation with the R.A.S.E. in 1887 when they were to be in Nottingham. Having decided to have no L.A.S. show, a £300 contribution was made to the R.A.S.E., particularly for Lincoln Longwool Sheep, and Blacksmiths from the County. That gave L.A.S. members free entry. The Society had tried a larger contribution, on condition that their members could have exclusive right to use the thoroughbred

Indicative of accord between town and countryside, the Stonebow in Lincoln decorated for Showtime in 1898. It was a growing city, factories and traders all operating in the great context of agriculture.

(Lincolnshire Library Service)

Stallion proposed to be sent into this County, plus a condition about the progeny of competing animals, but the R.A.S.E. refused.

Chemical Analysis was a service that had been maintained for members — Dr Voelcker (R.A.C., Cirencester, later of the R.A.S.E.) was retained as Consulting Chemist. He dealt with artificial manures, soils, waters, minerals, stones, oilcakes, bone dust, feeding meals, maize products, superphosphates, fish manure, soot, and lime. He produced analyses and opinion for this and other Societies. A contribution had been made to the Royal Agricultural Society in a law case about adulteration of feeding stuffs.

The Society gave evidence to Government in 1895 of the depression in farming. They reported that there was no friction, that landlords and tenants were on the best of terms, landlords having met tenants over rent levels most fairly. This applied especially to the larger landlords, Mr Chaplin having acted "most handsomely". Many tenants, however, said that rents were not reduced soon enough. The evidence concerning the land itself was that the clay lands had all gone back, but the Wolds had not. The Heath was not farmed quite so well, the Stamford district had deteriorated considerably. The larger farms were better than the smaller ones because more sheep were kept on them. Some farms had been reduced in size, a very small amount was in owners' hands, but no land had been abandoned.

Ancient and modern in the new century

Brigg Exhibition of 1901, the 32nd Show, was in a more prosperous era. The Society had moved through nearly all the hazards of survival, from weather affecting the number of visitors, pre-show contributions varying, Swine Fever affecting pig entries, social change in the departure from the County of some greater supporters, and the deaths of some. Now, however, the membership was down to 68 Life and 898 Annual.

The Edwardian years early this century represented in the Shows a remarkable spread of farming techniques in the availability of implements, from ox harrow to oil engine; indeed in 1914 the first motor car at the Show — a Studebaker with a six seat torpedo touring body. The power plants for farms included steam, gas, paraffin and oil, and electric lighting plants were coming in. By 1908 Hornsby alone had a large oil engine erecting shop.

Membership remained sluggish, the lowest point being 70 Life and only 773 Annual Members in 1910. Yet the public luncheon was overcrowded, a larger marquee being considered for the future. Nor did it appear to lower confidence — of exhibitors and visitors. "One of the most successful" was Boston in 1902, even though it was not as before in the centre of the town. Ruin could have been the result if the Skegness Show of 1912 had had to be cancelled because of a foot-and-mouth standstill order. Animals had to be returned while on the way, Irish cattle already in the showground were under observation. It was decided "almost unanimously" to have no stock at all, and the Society got through with a loss of only £87.00.

The growth in this period was particularly in the remedies: in herbals, gripe mixtures, fly gall ointment, the flockmaster's friend, cough balls for different stock, but there was no falling off in other categories of wares; in fact a few new ones appeared.

Following Canada's lead, which they continued, the tempting of emigrants to the New World was pursued here by Queensland Government (1908), Western Australia (1906, 1911), Orient Line (1911), British South Africa (1914), and the Canadian Northern Railway (1914). "Own your own home, buy a farm for little more than the rent you now pay in a year" was the Canadian exhortation.

Stands on new themes came in — the Lincolnshire Curly Coated Pig Breeders Association (1908); unfortunately four years later there was confusion because they had not been marked and numbered. A "capital" site was provided in 1911 for a Nature Study Exhibition, which proved popular, and a propaganda tent for the National Service League (1912). Also in 1912 (Brigg) it was necessary to approach those "who had the management of the Flying Machine to prohibit any flying over the Showground. There would also be danger in the evening to the shedding and the horses within". The R.S.P.C.A. arrived in 1914, concerning humane treatment of animals and relieving their suffering; and the Boston and District Agricultural Union.

The Secretary, Mr Upton, died in 1906 after 37 years service. He had also been Secretary of four other organisations, including the Lincoln Red Shorthorn Association, and the Longwool Sheep Breeders. Then there was the Lincolnshire Chamber of Agriculture, which had been started in 1867 chaired by the Hon. A. L. Melville and Colonel Cracroft Amcotts. Its basis was the Agricultural Societies and Farmers' Clubs. Its purpose was as a political information and

Wm. Foster & Co. Ltd. threshing machine publicity. Original by J. Hassall, known for the Skegness "Jolly Fisherman".

(J. W. Ruddock & Sons Ltd)

pressure group, its first policy being to urge that there be a Minister for Agriculture. The fourth was the Horse Poisoning Prevention Association, part of attempts to stop the administering of the most vicious quack remedies to horses, including arsenic in some quantity, all in the chemical guesswork of the time. Even the death penalty early in the century had not stopped it.

Mr William Frankish was appointed as Secretary. He was on the Council of the R.A.S.E., and an Alderman on Lindsey

County Council. Perhaps it was due to him that the timber for shedding and stands was from this time hired, not as before, bought, used, and sold. The other Societies were asked, and agreed, to contribute. There were ten markets now which were to be attended to obtain subscriptions, and the fairs of Lincoln, Boston, and Caistor. The printed matter relative to each Show had become a Stock Catalogue of 96 pages, plus writing paper throughout for notes. the Implement Catalogue of 124 pages plus 12 pages of colour inserts; List of Premiums and Prizes 48 pages; Catalogue of Harness and Jumping Classes 8 pages; a music programme of 20 pages, all followed by the Report at 128 pages. The Horticultural side had its own schedule of 12 pages.

Constant contribution and encouragement continued from the family so closely associated, now represented by the Rt. Hon. the Earl of Yarborough, P.C., D.L., J.P., M.A., F.A.S., M.F.H., Vice-Admiral of Lincolnshire.

The forward-looking farmer could hardly be better served than by what was placed before him in these years. Eight makes of steam traction engine, a steam tractor, steam waggons, a road roller, portable and fixed steam engines; then oil engines by Crossley, Campbell, Robey, Tangye, gas engines, and several thrashers. All other equipment was there — statements were constantly made, such as "never exceeded in numbers, interest, or value". Famous names were present, Massey Harris, Deering, Melotte, Ransomes and the local ones. It had developed further as the task of agents rather than manufacturers to show the smaller implements. There was more of everything. In 1908 there were 153 stands and 1457 items. Lighting plants for the farmhouse and buildings could be by coal gas (Porter & Co. and Ruston, Proctor), or Acetylene Gas (by Peacock & Binnington; today the earliest constant exhibitor, from 1898). While the British Petroleum Company appeared (1912) with oil and fuel, and with sprayers, for travel one could buy a Spring Rully, or several other types. Then, as now, the use of implements depends on acreage, but their prolific use must have progressed to well below the 300 acre farm considered the general minimum sized user in 1881.

The stand of Marshall's of Gainsborough in 1911 at Brigg. Established in 1848, by 1914 their works were forty acres, with 5,000 workmen.

Stock kept up in interest, with inevitable variations from year to year. "Classes were well filled except Sheep and Pigs. The latter scarcely any from this County." "New classes, limited entry." "Lincoln Reds excellent." "Excellent except Hackney" — the hackney classes were considered for dropping three or four times. "Poultry down but July not favourable to them." "Opposition elsewhere for driving classes, so not so good as hoped for." "Shires a wonderful good show." "Breeding Hackneys disappointing again. Eight in, only three for judging."

Social change had been slight, the servants and labourers entries were maintained commensurate with employment on the land. Premiums had been correspondingly reduced.

There was no Show in 1907 because the Royal Show was in Lincoln, the previous time being 1854. This location was largely influenced by Sir Gilbert Greenall, M.F.H. (The Belvoir). A one day showing of L.A.S. classes with prizes for

L.A.S. members only was linked in, which attracted a splendid entry. Much help was given by Sir John Thorold, who was also on the R.A.S.E. Council.

In 1914 the Chairman, the Hon. Richard P. Stanhope had to leave to join H.M. Forces by the time the Annual Report was being agreed. A date for 1915 was fixed, but it was "to be further considered". In the event, the subsequent Show was five years later.

The internal combustion takeover

Over the years the Society represents agricultural development as it is presented to Lincolnshire farmers. There is no more sharp impact and example of this than the forty-fifth and forty-sixth shows, in 1920 and 1922. The wartime gap of five years had been a period of urgent technical development, with production and maintenance skills to match. For a further generation existing equipment would be running, but it was obvious that petrol and oil were to be the prime movers. It was already in the minds of the purchasers — steam equipment turned up in 1920, but dwindled thereafter.

Mechanical traction in this first post-war show was represented by the Titan tractor of International Harvester, a Wallis tractor manufactured by Ancona Motor Co. and Ruston, Proctor, the "Glasgow" tractor by James Wallace, a "Garner" Austin, and a Fiat. There was a Moline motor plough and tractor; the Midwest Engine Co. had the "Utilitor" tractor, "a one man outfit to do the work of one horse"; and Saunderson's "Universal", which had won the R.A.S.E. silver medal. Steam was represented by Ruston and Hornsby (now amalgamated) and Clayton & Shuttleworth, both of whom also offered internal combustion engines. Foster exhibited steam only — a portable, and a lorry.

Motor lorries were there by A.E.C., Garner, Dearborn (with a body by Grimsby Motors Ltd), and the "Vulcan" and the Ford chassis. The Lincolnshire Motor and Electric Tractor Co. Ltd showed the Ford touring car and other Ford products, and for cars the variety included the Darracq, the Hampton, and the Eric Campbell. Frank Allen Ltd of Brigg fully expressed these times by having two tractors, two motor bodies, and two traps. C. Kendall of Grimsby offered a Char-a-banc. There were nine petrol, oil, or paraffin stationary engines. Electric motors were offered by the County Borough of Grimsby. The new industry of accessories for all these was fully represented. A newcomer was Flax Cultivation Ltd., to urge the production of flax and flax products. In fact, a revival, because flax spinning was active in the county in the eighteenth century.

The interest of the farming community after a five year absence was expressed in the record entrance receipts. Inflation played its part, but it was an astonishing achievement. Trains were still meagre and transport generally for assembling the Show and getting to it was difficult. The Amusement Tax of £1374 was disputed, but had to be paid. All this with a total of 733 members. For 1921 it was fully hoped to be at Lincoln. Industrial stagnation, the dark agricultural outlook and industrial unrest were the basis of the decision to abandon the Show. The expenditure the year before had been "staggering" and the bills for labour had been "colossal". Instead they sent some money to help smaller local shows and the Royal Show. It did not impress the membership, which dropped in spite of an appeal to them not to let the lack of a show influence them. The next year a new continuity began, a run of eighteen shows to 1939.

It resumed at Skegness. The general exhibits dropped severely to 116 stands, but still included were all the small implements of husbandry. For many years there had been stands of bodies not directly connected with agricultural production, and this Show was no exception. The Daily Mail put up a Rest Tent, the Hull papers took a stand. The Lindsey County Federation of Women's Institutes showed their work and products. Coal, coke, gas lamps, billard tables and the like continued.

The stock, the competitive side of animal husbandry, continued with the same basic organisation as heretofore. The opportunity of the wartime gap was taken not to revive the hackney class. The return of the shows did not produce a flood

71

of frustrated entries: Hunters were down, and there was no jumping. Shires dropped even more, perhaps reflecting the use of machinery. There was no wool, and no poultry. It resulted, however, in the largest increase in the balance ever, at £115.6.9., even after some expenditure on sheep and pig pens. Costs had been brought down in the wake of government arrangements for the national crisis. Societies had negotiated together to obtain exemption from Amusement Tax — on educational grounds — otherwise there would have been a loss. Withdrawal of that Tax allowed funds for the return of Bands.

Inter-war survival 1923 to 1939

Patrons and President continued to be of the traditional kind. Vice-Presidents also, but now a few companies were included. (Nowadays they are personally represented). The Earl of Yarborough was Patron until 1936, and then it was the Lord Brownlow. The President throughout was the Rt. Hon the Earl of Ancaster. The Marquis of Lincolnshire, G.C.M.G., became a Vice-President.

Every period, indeed every Show, has transitional elements. This inter-war time of financially unassisted agriculture and definite trade depression nevertheless still shows the growth of the characteristics of modern agriculture and Shows.

In 1923, some sixty years ago, was the first Car Park, called a "Motor Garage and Cycle Park". It was run by the R.A.C., for charges. The R.A.C. duly produced small route maps to go with the catalogues. That year the Rt. Hon. Viscount Chaplin died. As Minister of Agriculture he had influenced Government to recognise cultivation of the land as the primary and principal industry of the Country. He had been a trustee of the society since 1869, fifty-four years.

Through the twenties and thirties the Society steered its way through losses and profits, over the period, managing to increase its assets, in spite of stagnant membership. When the figure was down to 630 annual and 95 life members it was regarded as "deplorable for a county like Lincolnshire". Even so the Show that year (1933) was most successful. June had proved to be a better month than July since 1925. Success was generally the result of no disease restrictions for stock, no upheavals, and good weather. Failure did not even result from the General Strike in 1926, when the Show was nearly abandoned, and thousands had to rely on road transport. Yet the year previous they had thought "the industrial population were taking less and less interest in agriculture". By 1934 the main item to note was the increase in "garage receipts".

Not many years passed without new challenge cups being presented, and constructive activity included a working dairy for the first time (1925), the continuance of the Light Horse Breeding Scheme, which obtained 33 new members (1935). From 1930 schoolchildren had been allowed to attend in groups. Within two years their numbers had grown to over seven thousand.

Those who had been connected with the early years of the Society were nearing the end of their days. In 1932 Mr John Evens retired as chairman of the stewards committee with hopes that the industry would be in better condition soon. In 1934 Sir Hickman Bacon, Bt. became chairman for the year — Having previously been chairman in 1883. After forty years on the Council E. H. Nevile of Skellingthorpe died. Deep regret was expressed in 1936 at the death of the Earl of Yarborough — Vice-President 1877, President 1880, Patron 1921. His interest had been keen, his support wholehearted, and the family sponsorship of Lincolnshire Agricultural Societies had continued over two centuries. In 1938 Mr Abel Smith also died, having joined in 1886. He was praised for his unflagging interest and ability, personal touch, and his great part in establishing the Society on a solid foundation.

Machinery exhibits were constantly increasing, especially to do with transport. Regular motor exhibitors were Chevrolet, Ford, Fiat, Bedford, Austin, and from 1937, Morris. They were mostly commercial, with vans, lorries and large chassis on offer. Names now defunct appeared, as Maxwell, Reo, GMC, Studebaker, Gilford, Commer, Dodge. It cannot be said that there was full representation of the vehicles available nationally.

Concomitant with this Shell-Mex, B.P., and Pratts High
Test petrol appeared, along with Dunlop stimulating the motor
age with products and public relations. Both the L.N.E.R. and
L.M.S.R. had their separate stands for information and
bookings at the beginning of the period. By its end they yielded
to sharing the same one.

Steam power was still represented, overwhelmed as it was
by internal combustion engines. Ransomes, Ruston &
Hornsby, Clayton & Shuttleworth, Foster, Marshall, Fowler,
Robey, all were shown several times. The finality was 1931
with Robey, 1932 for Ransome, 1934 for Marshall. Due to the
pleasant persistence of Mr Armitage, the Foster traction
engine and its thrashing equipment continued to appear, lastly
in 1939.

Additions to the pattern

The conditions of farming have so altered since the nineteen
thirties that it is satisfactory to find that the Shows of the
Society have not only brought in the new aspects, but have also
maintained at a greater level the basic and original purposes.
Farmers ceased to be taxable on a proportion of rental values
only, from 1948 being drawn into business rules. The National
need for food production and its import-saving, brought
guarantees, grants and subsidies. Again, engineering and
chemical research developed labour-saving operations and
heavier yields.

It is appropriate to take a Show comparison of 1939 with
1956. The latter year Sleaford had the last but two of the
travelling exhibitions, and the last in one of the old locations. It
was also the time when the present era was consolidating.
Since 1900 productivity had already doubled twice, with better
seeds, fertilisers, tractors, and less and less keep needed for
working horses. Self propelled operations allowed further
progress. The numbers employed were set to decline faster as
larger farms became thus easier to work and small farms could
not afford the equipment.

The changing pattern of Trade Stands:

Number of Stands

	1939	1956	1969	
Seeds	2	6	3	*More might have been*
Fertilisers	32	7	10	*expected in the past.*
Feeds	21	16	6	*This decrease may*

reflect the increase in arable, and in part amalgamated companies.

Medicinal	14	8	1	*Fewer stock may be a*

reason for the decrease, but especially more professionalism. Researched chemical remedies became available only from 1935.

Implements, equipment	67	92	68	*The increase in 1956*
and machines				*reflected in part more motor vehicles.*
Constructional	13	34	13	*New buildings for new*

needs led to the unsuitable older structures falling out of use. There is a substantial proportion of the smaller types. The major rush is over.

Totals:	120	163	101

The above are directly relevant to farming. There were also these categories:

	1939	1956	1969	
Domestic, Retail	30	32	69	*This category has been*
and Crafts				*present for many years, but latterly with great expansion.*
Educational,	10	51	75	*Government and County*
Propaganda,				*Council Departments assume a greater role.*
Finance,				*Influence on quality standards laid down*
Insurance,				*by legislation is a major factor. In 1956,*
Merchants				*some 16 of these were Banks, Finance, Merchants and Publications. Societies and Organisations seek members, and to influence. The industry has more and more to absorb.*

Totals:	40	83	144

At the County Show at Gainsborough in 1934. From the left: Mr J. H. Y. Henson, the Duke of Gloucester, Mr C. E. Howard, the Earl of Yarborough, Sir Hickman Bacon, and Mr R. Chatterton.

(Mr W. G. Henson)

Shortly after the 1939 show at Bourne preparations were made to see the Society through the war. No shows were held. Members were appealed to for continuance of their subscriptions, the challenge cups were lodged for safety in the National Provincial Bank, the plant was put into store in the Society's shed at Bourne for periodic inspection, (the more valuable items being moved in 1942 to a brick building at Morton). The chairman of the Finance Committee, Col. H. G. Dean, was called away for military service some days before the outbreak of war, a small retaining fee was arranged for the clerk of the works, and a grant to the office clerk who was with the armed forces. The secretary offered to subtract any wartime salary he may obtain from that paid to him by the society. Some grants were made annually, more particularly to the Red Cross in the towns where shows had been held, but not in 1940 to the Hunter Improvement Society for their travelling stallion. It was at first thought that membership was being retained, but by 1944 there was no pleasure in the report that annual subscribers numbered 486 only. From then, however, there was continual improvement.

Col. O. S. Nelthorpe first mentioned post-war needs in November 1942 — seeds — stock — and the first show for after the war. The next year such thought was spreading, with talk of Britain being looked on as before, as the stud farm of the world. It was to be two years after that, however, in 1945, when it was decided to have a one day show in 1946, the Royal Show in Lincoln having been postponed to 1947. The meeting was sadly overshadowed with great regret at the death of Mr C. E. Howard, member since 1904, and on the Council from 1907, and chairman of Stewards and Finance Committees.

The end of the war was a difficult time, though staff returned, Fred Taylor being back as Secretary, and R. Hallam as clerk. Some plant was still at Bourne, and there were shortages of paper, timber, labour, and so much uncertainty. Yet in the atmosphere of hope, for the first time since 1893 membership had grown to over a thousand.

Until 1950 the Patron was the Earl Brownlow, to be succeeded by the present Earl of Ancaster. The constant and long-standing connection with the past was also maintained by Lord Yarborough being a Vice-President and the Lord Heneage taking offices of President and Chairman. Vice-Presidents now included 24 individuals, 4 Banks, 2 Companies, the Lincolnshire Farmers Union, and the Lincolnshire Automobile Club.

The nature of the Annual Show envisaged by the founders of the earlier Societies — mainly for stock — was more closely approached in 1946 than in the previous hundred years or any recent year. The one day Show at Blankney took place, getting things going again at an early date. It was virtually of animals only, with only forty trade stands. No poultry, no horticulture, no implements. Shires, Hunters, Suffolks, Percherons, Dairy

Cows, were shown. There were Heavy turnouts and short sharp Scurry Stakes, with competitions for milking, shoeing, welding, and Beet. The attendance was good, in spite of the distance. For his generous help Mr Parker was invited to become an Honorary Life Vice-President. It was a Show which reinforced the need for proper road transport handling, the car parking organisation having been so bad that the contractors had ultimately waived their charge, but the Society paid them half. Two years later Shows built up to 258 Exhibitors of Stock, with 773 animals, but "trade" stands (not called "implement" stands any more) had increased to 137. Two years after that the latter increased again to 233, then a record.

Hounds were paraded, as for many years; two one-day cricket matches were part of the entertainment at Stamford in 1950; motor cycle displays, Sheepdogs; inter-Hunt jumping, a Military band — these were some of the organised attractions. In 1948 was included a Dog Show, but nothing approaching the size of the 1926 one of the Louth and District Canine Society, which achieved a catalogue of one hundred pages. There have also been trotting races, and pushball on horseback.

The background of material progress was represented by combines replacing threshers (even the spelling of that had changed). They had been invented a century before in California, became self-propelled first in 1908, and were adapted for corn much later. They led to a need for corn driers. The 1948 Show first saw the Minneapolis Moline Combine Harvester; in 1950 a locally made grain drier appeared, by Penney & Porter. Artificials and sprays began to render the rotation of crops obsolescent. Ferguson tractors, with their "complete farm system" were also shown from 1948, milk sterilising equipment arrived, along with crop sprayers, irrigation, tubular steel buildings and pea machinery. It was a pea sorter which won one of the three Society Silver Medals for new or improved appliances in 1956.

During these immediate post-war years, the outstanding new feature was organised in conjunction with the Lindsey, Kesteven, and Holland War Agricultural Executive Committees. Farm competitions were held, to include ploughing, beet-gapping, milking, plashing, draining and ditching. The chairman was Mr H. Jones, later chairman of the Stewards amongst other of his functions for the Society. These competitions took on a life of their own, with luncheons at the Saracen's Head in Lincoln for the Executive and Competition Committees and judges. Discussion took place on the lines of timing, limiting of entries by standards, and whether it was the best farmed farm or the best crops that were being judged. In 1951 the National Agricultural Advisory Service were ordered not to continue with the work, a main reason for the ultimate cessation of the competitions. Mr H. Jones, also having been on the Council since 1920, and Honorary Director from 1946, died in 1954. In the latter office he was succeeded by Mr E. M. Howard who had worked closely with him.

Some long-lasting decisions were made which have become part of the face of the Society, small as the matters may have appeared at the time. Reconsideration in changed social circumstances of Farm Worker classes was one matter, another was the provision to each member of a complimentary ticket for a lady. A members' lawn was to be provided, from 1949. All this time the Society was gaining strength, with nineteenth century numbers of membership being surpassed. By 1947 it became 1350, and 2265 in 1949, and then there was thought still to be considerable scope. Expansion began to overtake resources, and with casual labour getting short members were asked if they could help with a man or two at the disposal of the stewards.

One of the most remarkable expressions of the Lincolnshire Agricultural Society is the constantly renewed personal enthusiasm which gives it the force to proceed and to develop. The path may look outwardly straightforward but even in years of Society prosperity there have been the hazards of weather affecting attendance, and of its diminishing the entries of stock, of a facility not being ready on time (or of the stand in 1950 at Stamford collapsing, resulting in unfavourable publicity). Disease is by no means eliminated, as the Belton Show of 1952, overlaid by Foot-and-Mouth restrictions, discouraging large numbers of potential visitors. Grass sown to carry the Show could fail. It was a considerable commitment to mount a Show, and each year was a renewal of commercial risk. Some seventy-five acres were now being needed and goodwill of landlords and tenants was vital, as at Scawby in 1953. In fact, the goodwill of others — Brigg Agricultural Society giving up its Show that year, and contributing to the fund. Grantham Agricultural Society had done the same two years previously. On the social side, Mr B. Leslie Barker got an ad hoc committee together and arranged a successful and popular Ball.

The Society continues through the losses of those who have shown so much support and dedication. Twenty eight years President, deep regret was felt at the death of the Rt. Hon. the Earl of Ancaster in 1950. The Lord Heneage had become a member of the Council in 1898, and the revival since 1946 was due much to his inspiration and energy. He died in 1954. Fifty-six years of loyalty and service in all were given by Mr F. P. Taylor, appointed in 1898, secretary since 1928, who died in 1954 in the regard and respect of all.

In its existence for the encouragement of agricultural improvement the Society is the vehicle in Lincolnshire, but it is not isolated. The premiums and prizes and medals offered have been for many years given by outside persons or organisations. Many societies assist or have assisted in this matter, such as the East Midlands Dairy Shorthorn Association, National Pig Breeders Association, National Horse Association, the Clydesdale Horse Society, the Large Black Pig Society, the Shire Horse Society, Societies for Essex Pigs, Suffolk Horses, Lincoln Red and British Friesian Cattle, the Aberdeen Angus Cattle Association, British Dairy Farmers, Lincolnshire Beekeepers, Hampshire Down Sheep Breeders, various Lincoln and other Sheep and Ram Associations. The full list is more extensive.

The circulation continued round the former towns, but additional locations were chosen, such as Blankney (1946), Belton Park (1948, most attractive, with the horse ring in front of the house, and 1952), Aswarby Park (1956), Brocklesby (1957), and Burtoft in 1958. It was significant that by now

Judging the Trade Stands in 1955; from the left: Mr Russell, Mr Wholey, Lord Heneage, Mr Joseph Nickerson, Lord Ancaster, Mr F. C. Townsend, Colonel Sutton-Nelthorpe, Mr S. Milligan-Manby.

there was no need for a populous locality to give support and that there was enough personal transport available to maintain attendance.

Lincolnshire land use, 1955

A study of the productive acreages of the county under the various agricultural headings and comparison with the rest of the United Kingdom shows Lincolnshire to have a creditable spread of all crops and livestock, except for the thin representation of orchards and small fruit. As a Society for the County this is its working basis and that of its competitors and exhibitors.

Not usually considered a stock area, the total cattle were of the average density of Eastern England, and dairy cattle compared with the East and the South. Milk production of

Lindsey was comparable with Herefordshire, Kesteven with Bedfordshire, Holland with Radnorshire. As to sheep, they were as widespread as in all English lowlands, and more than in East Anglia. Pigs had average distribution. Slaughtering of pigs, cattle and sheep was comparable with Gloucestershire.

Lincolnshire is the Country's predominant but not exclusive potato area. They are particularly on the flat lands. Wheat was the average of East Anglia; it was heaviest in the Fens, which produced the biggest yields in the country. It thins off gradually to the West Country. Barley was spread as much as anywhere except East Anglia. Oats were average, Lancashire and Aberdeenshire being highest, but the greatest yield per acre was in Holland. Average were fodder roots and green crops; poultry were average; sugar beet was somewhat less than East Anglia. There was a very strong showing of vegetables, flowers, and nursery stock, especially in the lowlands, the most concentrated area in the country. Missing from the modern age, however, are the prodigious number of geese decoyed and sent to London in their thousands for eating. An industry for quills and mattresses was sustained by plucking two or three times a year.

This comprehensive background on different soils influences attitudes to development requirements, to the purpose and end use of crops, the capital in the machinery, and animal breeding. Whatever the change in emphasis since 1955, the categories remain in force. And the social, sporting and cultural aspect of the farming community cannot be omitted from the show days.

The single location, 1959

The fourth Show before the adoption of a permanent showground was on one of the grounds that had been considered for that purpose. The West Common at Lincoln gave its answer. Negative. Once again preparations had been hindered by bad weather, over Autumn, Winter and Spring, with a very heavy storm in the heavy traffic time of the three days preceding the Show. There were several inches of flood, tractors had to help vehicles, vast quantities of ash, gravel, and straw were spread. Good humour prevailed in the operatives, and the attendance was only a little below average.

The three Shows following could have dispelled any anxiety about the annual move. There was pleasure and pride in the goodwill and generous support of the neighbourhood at Aswarby. This success of a 43,000 attendance in 11,500 vehicles was at a ground previously thought to be unsuitable. The following year Brocklesby provided a perfect background. Fuel restrictions limited the entries, thus bringing a new problem, but after doubt about proceeding the Society thought that it could face any vicissitude with confidence. The other shortage, of water, was overcome by the Fire Service. The Show in 1958 on the land of Mr A. H. Carter at Burtoft concluded five years at an average profit of £3,500. The money was being spent on equipment which would have permanent use. It was a period when each stand needed more services, and improved buildings were necessary for stock, for exhibitors and members.

It had been in the different context of hoping to produce "very material savings" that a permanent showground was first discussed on 1st June 1945. Subscribers were down to 613, from 7,500 farmers in Lincolnshire. "One thousand more would add £500". There was reluctance to increase entrance fees — though "a shilling would add a thousand pounds, and wages had about doubled since 1939, and farming had not been unprofitable". It was expressed that to hold the Show in one place, however, would not encourage local funds, and attendance may fall off; from experience it was agreed that two days instead of three would not help much. Lincoln was the only practicable centre.

The upshot was to seek to acquire a redundant aerodrome within easy range, and with a convenient railway station. (Having depended on it for so many years, this was the last time the railway was ever mentioned). After stating that the Chairman was to investigate such a place with the military authorities the minute was somewhat negatived by its last three words, namely "(there is none)".

The sub-committee which was formed did consider the West Common in Lincoln, which was at that time thought to be promising. In what was a difficult time for the Society the committee then examined and considered all policy at length under each heading.

The sub-committee met the Mayor of Lincoln and Councillors on 22nd June, 1945, and thought that the south-east corner of the West Common would be excellent, just except that the Grand Stand would be of no use, as it was too far away. The plan of the 1931 Show was considered the most suitable. It was only the basic ground that was in mind — permanent buildings were expensive and even concrete floors were thought to be costly. Among those on the committee were those who were to play such a great part as the subject developed — Col. O. S. Nelthorpe, and Mr E. M. Howard.

Confidence grew as the Society began to return to success, and three years later in 1948 the matter was "left for the time being". Future grounds for the Show were being considered for the next few years — Revesby, Scunthorpe, Gainsborough, Stamford, Gosberton, and hope of four more. After an outstanding successful Show in Belton Park that year it was noted that suitable and adequate showgrounds were increasingly difficult to find. It was believed, however, that it was the general wish to continue to take the Show round the County. There were no longer many places where twenty-five acres of grass could be found, with as much again for car parking. The next year it also became clear that record weights of traffic would soon overload countryside roads.

It was Lincoln City which made the next move, six years later in 1954, by suggesting that some of their land adjoining the West Common might be suitable, and it was inspected. By August 1955 other inspections had been made but nothing suitable had yet been found. After three years of bad weather a preliminary budget for roads was drawn up. It was now agreed to find a permanent site, and the Air Ministry and Land Commissioner were asked. The idea this time was to establish a site gradually and to go round to other places perhaps every three years. There were still doubts about the level of attendance at a permanent site, on a personal transport base.

Internal roads were now essential — they had been given by local companies at Scawby in 1953, and the necessity for them at Swineshead in 1954, and their general absence on park and farm land, had convinced Council in the terms that "they would soon be compelled to abandon taking the Show round the County, and acquire a permanent Showground. It may be prudent to decide now to look for one". A sub-committee was appointed to find a site and to make an immediate purchase.

1956 — hope to find a suitable site soon. 1957 — no substantial progress yet. Other Societies had succeeded. The Show was at Brocklesby this year, and in view of the difficulties Lord Yarborough would allow the Society to come a second year if required. The matter of the permanent site had been with Estate and Farm Agents, it had been in the Press, but of many places inspected, none was adequate. One had been near Woodhall Spa, but the committee preferred to be near Lincoln; there had been Skellingthorpe Airfield, but it was to be taken by the city for housing (the city offered to divide it); and just north of Lincoln at Burton the area was 80 acres, but 150 acres were wanted. The neighbour would not sell. Burton Lane End was low lying, and not owned locally.

Ultimately the choice of site was reduced to three. Land in Nettleham parish adjoining the Riseholme Farm Institute was considered, but it was undulating and could not be recommended. The former airfield of Dunholme Lodge was examined but it was split in ownership, it was too small, nor was it level. During 1957 the suggestion had been made by Mr E. W. Barker and the secretary, Mr Shelley, that the place which is now the location could well suit. The President, Lord Ancaster, approached the owner, Lord Monson, on the subject, and discussions began. The Executive Committee of 11th February, 1958, debated the matter. Ten members were present, including the President, under the chairmanship of Col. O. S. Nelthorpe. Mr Howard explained that the site was level, freely drained with the exception of one small part, flat as anywhere, and services were available except special arrangements would have to be made for water because the existing main only just served Scampton airfield. One hundred and sixty acres were needed. The owner would sell because it was for the Society.

The meeting was characterised by Mr Howard maintaining the factual background, and the chairman steering the meeting away from the difficulties towards agreement to proceed. There were lesser questions raised; about planners, aircraft take-off needs of Scampton, the possible rates, cropping and tenantright. The major matter was the price of the land, which was being offered at more than its farming value. The new use was not to be a farming one, but it produced much objection, because that was the value that was understood, and its existing use. Land was increasing in price beyond the experience of the past. Money could be lost on this land; that amount should not be paid for this type of land; could the vendor leave some on loan; too much an acre; leave part for now; perhaps an option on part. A major point was that Society investments had gone down, and this land had gone up. "Could not be a worse time." "Land as high as it can be." "Put it off a year or two."

The Chairman remarked on the savings on roads and fences; that if the value went down it was not dangerous because they had no debts; there was nowhere else; agreed it was expensive but other sites were the same price; worthwhile to save on subsequent moves; moving the Show about was not easy. Social conditions had developed so much that no-one mentioned that the R.A.S.E. had tried a single site at Park Royal from 1903 to 1905. Attendance had dropped to a quarter, and circulation had to be resumed. (One of their problems was typified in Lincoln in 1907, when gas mains laid for the Show were one and a quarter miles, and of water mains four miles.)

Mr Howard was by no means confident that there would be a decision to go ahead. "Shows were dropping off; perhaps it could be the East Midlands Society", he propounded. The resolution to proceed, proposed by Mr A. H. Carter, was ultimately passed with continuing talk of negotiation, which was not possible. Members fundamentally agreed with Mr B.

86

L. Barker that they had to go on, and talk turned to practicalities of its use. The Chairman thought the sooner it was done the better, because they had been three years already. Negotiation was dropped out of the proposition. On 21st February, 1958, the Council accepted the call for action. There was some hope expressed of reducing the price because of the Land Tax of £5.7.0. and the tithe of £34.10.0. (which was redeemed in 1965).

A major Agricultural Society

Shows had moved from place to place in Lincolnshire for one hundred and twenty-one years, excluding the twelve of the early society in Lindsey. Since 1869 with this society each town had had its fair share for its size and location. Scunthorpe managed two, having come into the circulation in 1928, grown from a village to over 32,000 population. Lincoln achieved eleven shows, whereas fifteen would have been every five years as promised by the North Lincolnshire Agricultural Society. There had been three locations away from any town.

There was no looking back after the choice of the permanent site, and no-one wished to do so. Enabled by the progress of negotiations work began on the site in May 1958. Hedges were removed round the five arable fields, cultivations were cleared, there was levelling to do (including the Roman road), surveys of soil structure, and samples, tree planting, water, fencing, telephones, electricity, and above all the requirement of a good sward and the roads. Seed was presented by the Corn and Seed Merchants Association, slag was given by the Appleby Frodingham Steel Corporation, the roads were made at cost by J. G. Eccles & Co. Ltd. and Clugston Cawood Ltd., the latter providing the surveyor. Boston Tractors loaned tractors and trailers.

An appeal for funds was considered, but was decided against, because reserves were adequate at the time. There was, however, still doubt in August whether the 1959 Show could be on the permanent ground instead of as previously planned on the Heath at Burton. It continued to be helped by members through work and gifts of material. There were many tokens of goodwill and support. Sadly, the Lord Monson had died just before the work began.

In three miles of avenue the first show there had a record 270 trade stands. There was "every conceivable item of agricultural merchandise" accompanied by "all the major breeds of horses, cattle, sheep and pigs". Included in the cattle were Lincoln Red Shorthorns; in the sheep were Lincoln Longwools; but in the pigs Lincolnshire Curly Coats were not represented. There had been twenty-eight of them the previous year at Burtoft but the Stewards thought it not enough, so the class was not offered. The L.C.C.P. Breeders Society protested in vain. It was suggested to them that the challenge cup be disposed to a double winner. The breed is now extinct.

The new site was thoughtfully planned. Detail was such that the Grand Stand was to face North or East; the Members' Enclosure must not cut off exhibitors; the public entrance should not come through the stock, which might be untidy. Marquees could give way in future to permanent building, the potential was recognised. Services for all could be provided without stint, and the maintenance of stock also requires them. There would not be much loss, if any. Those who exhibited every few years when the Show was nearby would not appear. For example, the Stamford Mercury exhibited at Stamford in 1950, and presumably they will not do it again, but it is a matter of sentiment that down to two centuries ago it was the vehicle in this County for advertising and reporting meetings and shows.

Thus, the seventy-sixth Show in 1959, was the first on the Permanent Showground, after thirteen months of planning and activity. The advantages of permanency were to be demonstrated in the traffic handling. While curiosity may have played a part, coupled with good weather, the Show attendance was probably a record at over 47,000 (including an estimate of ticket holders, and with many visiting on both days). The number of cars arriving was certainly the highest ever at 15,100. After some years with no alteration, the admission price had been doubled to ten shillings.

Settled as it is, the secretary was not very pleased at the start to be prompted by the C.P.R.E about the planting of trees. He thought the status of the Society was such that he need give no further assurance of their intention to produce a fitting setting for their Shows and an aesthetic appearance of the site. The offices were still in Guildhall Street in Lincoln, not many yards from where had been the Rein Deer Inn, the meeting place of a former Society.

Today

The Society is not without competition round the county boundary, for it is in all four compass directions. It comes from Societies which have all continued from about 1800 without the changes which took place in Lincolnshire. (The Norfolk Show even has posters within ten miles of Lincoln).

The Society is an unincorporated charitable body for the furtherance of agriculture, the organisation of the annual show, and the support of other events and organisations to these ends. Maybe not all breeds and breeders, manufactures and manufacturers appeared at the shows, but over more than a century no trend has gone unrepresented. In earlier years what was offered was directly related to the farmers personal work, of assistance to the physical operations. The link was close between the stock and the farm produce. Today, with so much coming from remote manufacture the total affinity of farm operations is lost. The research in Government and industry is far removed from the former discussions in markets. Formerly there was an implement catalogue as large as that for the stock, but now there is none. It must be significant of the feeling. It may be a matter for congratulation that after generations and revolutions in agriculture the image is that of a Stock Show still, with only ten per cent of the catalogue devoted to other matters. Without some of those others, however, the stock would be as badly fed as a century ago.

Agricultural progress is as a whole. New ways have to overtake existing commitments, and progress is uneven. For example, milk standards have improved out of recognition in the last thirty years. But the government official of the National Dairy Service in 1948 in Hackthorn lived opposite the dairy of Mr Waby, who took the milk straight from the cow round the village, serving it directly from the bucket, proud of its freshness and warmth. Now dairying needs harvesters, unloaders, feeders and waterers, cleaners, milkers, coolers, pick-ups, pasteurisers, bottlers and butter and cheese making machines. And chemists come in on pastures, fertilisers, grasses, conditioners, pelleted feeds, sprays, and artificial breeding. All stockbreeding and all farming have to acknowledge mechanical and chemical needs. It is said that the adoption of ideas moves northward through the country. Certainly in Lincolnshire there is no lack of farmers looking for the next improvement. Quotations of a few years ago are: "If you can't do it by machine it can't be done"; "rotation is not necessary now to preserve the land"; "what I do now with twelve men I will be able in ten years to do with three". Overall the labour on farms reduced from 1,500,000 in 1871 to 693,000 in 1960 (the labour outside the industry making this possible is not assessed). The aeroplane, which they feared would frighten the horses at Brigg in 1912 is now a farm implement; the wireless which was first exhibited for entertainment in 1923 is now a means of farm communication; the electricity of electric light plants seventy years ago is an indispensable farm force.

In April 1982 the Agricultural Show Exhibitors Association praised four Societies for the proper image of their Shows, of which the Lincolnshire was one. This was because the main purpose of agricultural business had not been usurped by the need to attract urban visitors. The pressures from retailers for turning it into more of a publicised market have to be resisted. Larger again, the ninety-ninth Lincolnshire Show some weeks later had the mix which is now general.

Where so many years ago most of those exhibitors present would be of the County, now there is much national representation, branches and subsidiaries. This broad characteristic is also strong in the exhibitors of the stock. The

Lincoln Reds in competition all have county ownership, all the Lincoln Longwools, and half the Goats, but of other stock local owners are much in the minority

Of the horses appearing in all classes only one in four are of Lincolnshire and South Humberside. It is the whole country position that influences success. With the showground at capacity, the machinery on view being second only to the Royal Show, and the stock numbers having increased, this Society is national.

The numbers of stands can be analysed as follows:

	Directly related to farming	Indirectly related to farming	Not related to farming*	
Machinery, equipment and its maintenance	86	—	—	17%
Feeds, fertilisers, chemicals, seeds	45	—	—	9%
Motors and trailers	21	24	—	9%
Animal Breeders	2	—	—	½%
Buildings, improvements	10	1	18	5½%
Public Bodies, Societies	19	12	30	12%
Ancillary Services	9	7	0	3%
Finance, Insurance	—	16	1	3%
Retailing	—	36	177	41%
	38%	18%	44%	100%

*(That is not to say that farmers and their wives are uninterested in improving their homes, receiving propaganda, or the generality of what can be purchased retail. It would seem, however, that to be sustained this category needs the numbers of general visitors.)

Overwhelmed as commercial stock in this part of England appears to be by arable prominence, there is still a basis for a mixed show. In Lincolnshire there are 170,000 cattle and calves, 300,000 sheep and lambs, 300,000 pigs, and 7,700,000 poultry. There are also 2,800 geese, and over half a million ducks. However, compared with a hundred years ago cattle and sheep are down to a quarter in number, but there are over three times as many pigs. Grassland then was forty per cent (permanent pasture thirty per cent) of the county, now it is twenty per cent, but that itself is more than 200,000 acres, which in a smaller county would provide an image of stock rearing. (It should be noted that today the large acreage for maintaining cart horses is not required.)

The prizes used to be about the measure of several weeks' wages of a farm worker. Today they equal a couple of days or less. On the selling side, the cost relative to the consumer's income has dropped since the middle nineteen-fifties, eggs and broiler chickens to a sixth and a fifth respectively, milk to less than a half.

There is a partnership between the farmer and the chemist certainly, and with the engineer and the banker, but perhaps government is the partner supreme in setting the context and the standard to which to work. Because of the extraordinary scientific progress of the last thirty-five years production overall has doubled again. Ever since William Pitt taxes have been put on and taken off, for example on horses to encourage the use of oxen; and production has been desired and then ignored in the name of imported cheap food, but this recent farming generation has been helped forward in the national interest as never before. The response has been effective from all. In the nineteen-thirties on average land it was just not possible to grow potatoes for the selling price; on good land, perhaps. There is much to build upon — it is the same recipe of recording, examining, testing, and researching. It is a far cry from the old thinking that the silver-grey rabbits on wold and heath were believed to help fertilise the soil. Much farm machinery is now shown as historic, firstly at the centenery show of 1969. Needs have become more detailed — like copper deficiency in sheep, fertiliser waste in application, biochemicals for yield, earlier maturity, and the constant search for fertility. As in 1796 farmers agree to try and then to report. In 1969 the Society started a new type inspection/ production class in the dairy section; then a new open class for beef recorded bulls of any breed to identify the best potential. The predominance of over a million acres of improving arable and horticultural crops in Lincolnshire is, however, not directly obvious to the visitor to the Annual Show. (Perhaps the area of the Society's influence is not contiguous with the County boundary, but overall the land use is similar.)

This new era and image was accompanied by redesign of badges and medals following upon the recent adoption of a crest. Hope was expressed that the large annual turnover of members would cease, but it is still a factor. Even so, since then the numbers have doubled. Lady Associate Membership was introduced. The dating of the Show had been considered once again, and because all of them could not be separated in the calendar it was accepted that it had to coincide with the Royal Highland and the Three Counties Shows. The formula for the Lincolnshire is that it is geared to the Royal Show, preferably to precede it. When the R.A.S.E. was looking for a permanent site Nottingham was one of the locations being considered, which caused anxious opposition here. A suggestion in committee that the R.A.S.E. might use the North Carlton site for a Show was not carried, in that it might be misunderstood.

Support in the single location was better than had been expected. Economies were realised, but in part obscured or counterbalanced by new factors, such as rates, maintenance of the ground throughout the year, and the improvements which were demanded. These last all came from own resources. A longer term plan was adopted, rather than waiting to see each year what the funds were. The programme was constantly reviewed by Mr E. M. Howard and Col. O. S. Nelthorpe. And development did go ahead, starting from the ground upwards by the need to remove thousand of stones. Solving the water supply problem was fundamental; redesigning the livestock section, stockmen's accommodation, seeking a right-of-way to Burton Road to help with the continually increasing motor traffic, a permanent building for President and members, lawns, plantings, fencing (partly against vandalism). For the Grand Ring improvement the soil was provided by the British Sugar Corporation of Brigg; A. Barker Excavators heaped the soil; twenty lorries were loaned by farmers; and Fox Plant Ltd excavated and relevelled the soil. This sort of assistance is part of the strength of the Society. It was improvement rather than development when entrance ticket machines were installed, because of "more than tolerable roguery" at one gate. With the Show ended, litter picking is a maintenance task, done some years by schoolchildren, once by R.A.F. Swinderby as a community project. The usual measure of work is for twenty pickers for three days, but machines now help the ground staff. In mounting a Show there is a recurring difficulty unrelated to agriculture — each year the entertainment programme has to be varied. Whether it is Bands and parades, decorated trailers by the Y.F.Cs., themes on horses, foxhounds, falcons, sheep dog or police dog displays, or parachutists, or a hot air balloon, a search every year, in the urge for variety, has to be made to discover something new. The racing camels from Longleat were sponsored by Lindsey & Kesteven Fertilisers Ltd., but another spectacular, the Roman Charioteers, could not come because they had had an accident. The Australian Axemen were a big hit. Newness is important for drawing visitors, as the Trade Standholders have on occasion urged. Once (1965) the programme grew to be too full, and the parade of cattle had to be cancelled, to the annoyance of the Lincoln Red Cattle Society. In 1972 the ring sequence was altered to fit in the television needs, but it proved to be too complicated to do it again. Mr J. E. Sanders as President in 1971 introduced coaching classes and combined driving. After four years they had to be dropped, because some competitors were precluded by the dates clashing with Ascot. Mr W. G. Henson directed Spillers Pony Show and Show Jumping Champion in co-operation with sponsorship by Yorkshire Television. Useful propaganda for farm safety was included with entertainment, highlighted in a machinery parade.

With the permanent location consolidated, it became a property for letting out for use by others, and a good source of increasing revenue. The first request was for International Sheep Dog Trials. Other functions which, like the Society, had hired odd fields now saw the ground's attractions — riding club, motor cycle club, traction engine rallies, archery, sales, and the buildings themselves are satisfying a social demand. The centenary of 1969 produced a substantial increase in members and in trade support, some of the latter now having a lien on their place. A Centenary Fund project was associated with a Building Demonstration area. The attendance of the Duchess of Gloucester continued that family's long interest in the Society; the Patron and President was the Rt. Hon. The Earl of Ancaster. So that the 1969 Annual Report could be the one hundredth, 1967 was not numbered at all, so as to omit one, the first being 1869. However, the notion fell through, and since then numbering has ceased.

Col. Oliver Sutton Nelthorpe, C.B.E., D.S.O., M.C., died in 1963. He had given unparalleled service for over thirty-five years, especially relative to re-establishment after the war, and to the change to the permanent showground. Chairman of committees and of the Council from 1954, he was first elected to it in 1927. In 1965 Brian Shelley left. He had been secretary for eleven years, with the difficulties of this period to overcome. He joined the Royal Norfolk Agricultural Association. His deputy, Donald Clark, took over. Mr John Evens died in 1966, having been on the Council from 1923. The Rt. Hon. The Earl of Yarborough died also that year, having been for long a Vice-President and Trustee. Mr P. Waddingham, of Louth, died in 1967, having served so well and loyally as Clerk of Works from 1909 to 1952, and also assisted after then. Through their guidance and work the Society had been maintained in one era and piloted through into another quite revolutionary change for new social circumstances.

It was September 1969 when Sir Weston Cracroft-Amcotts decided to relinquish the office of Chairman. He reported on an encouraging increase in membership, but that the annual attendance was not improved. Farmworkers were less inclined to come as it could affect earnings on piecework. (There were also fewer of them). Winter lecture or village outings were suggested as possibilities for encouraging their interest.

Sir Weston was asked if he would become President, to which he replied that he would like to consider the matter. It was the Society about which he was thinking, and not his personal position. Shortly afterwards he wrote that he would accept, but he wished to be assured that the office would be annual, by a new nominee each year. He suggested rules: that the person should be resident in the County, and must know he was to be nominated. The committee agreed with these points, but not as inviolate with another, that the retiring president should be consulted. The committee preferred to be free to make ad hoc decisions, and members' suggestions of further rules — about long service, or donations to the Society — were not accepted as policy. Sir Weston became the first Annual President for 1970, and his reorganisation thus enables a variety of prominent persons to bring their influence and interest continually to bear.

It was a sad occasion when on the eve of the 1970 Show the newly elected Chairman, E. Maxwell Howard, Esq., C.B.E., died after a short illness. He was an outstanding agriculturalist, nationally known and respected, having served on a wide variety of agricultural bodies. Elected to the Council and the Finance Committee in 1944, Stewards Committee in 1950, and later its Chairman, for sixteen years Honorary Director. The Society elected him in 1954 to Life Membership of the Council, in 1958 with Life Vice-Presidency. To commemorate him are the entrance gates to the Pavilion lawn. The next generation now takes its place with his son Mr C. E. N. Howard as Hon. Treasurer.

In the guise of Value Added Tax an imposition was placed upon charges, in a more comprehensive form than the Amusement Tax of fifty years previously. Once again Societies combined to dispute its applicability, and once again argument was followed by its impact being modified. The general progression in subsequent years had been one of record results — of surplus, of unprecedented demand for stands so that the ground is now full — yet it is all accompanied by matching increase in expenditure. Twenty more acres purchased bring the area to one hundred and eighty-three all told — the extra being obtained for cars and lorries. The flow is such that neighbours Mr Marris and Lord Monson's estate give willing assistance in the need. The intermixing of maybe

Opposite: The judging of Shire horses is early in the day's activities at the 1980 Show. (Lincolnshire Echo)

thirty thousand people on the Showground at any one time is the measure to which needs must be arranged. All generations make up the visitors including those attracted to the Children's Farmyard Section, and for even lesser ages the creche so pleasantly provided by the W.V.S. Voluntary organisations play their essential part — the St. John Ambulance Brigade, the British Red Cross Society, Girl Guides and Boy Scouts.

Within all the disparate happenings the first purpose of the former "Anniversaries" continued: medals and premiums, some to Farm Institute students, to exhibitors of new or improved implements, awards for stock and for stands. Some grants have been added to outside objects, such as to the British Field Sports Society, to the Queen's Silver Jubilee Fund, the U.K. Farming Scholarships Trust. These are all to agricultural interests, as may be proper — it was refused in 1964 as unprecedented that money should be sent to the Cathedral Restoration Fund (actually a contribution had been made in 1940).

In accordance with the resolution of over one hundred years previously the new Lord Lieutenant, Mr Henry Nevile, in 1976 was asked and agreed to become the Patron of the Society. He was also President for that year owing to the tragic death of Mr Leslie Barker in a motor accident in February, who had been elected only three months previously. In 1977 Mr C. L. Bembridge resigned as Chairman after having taken an "almost daily interest" in Society affairs for forty-three years of service "one way and another". On the Council from 1934, Stewards Committee from 1947, Honorary Director from 1969, Chairman from 1973, and after relinquishing that office, President in 1980. The executive committee recommended that Mr H. P. Kelway should succeed him as chairman. Chartered Accountant ànd Corn Merchant, the appointment demonstrates both honour and freshness, in that it is the first time a chairman has not been directly involved in farming itself.

Since 1981 the Society base has been at the Showground, a secretarial building having been donated by the Joseph Nickerson Charitable Foundation, the secretary since

December 1979 being Mr Joseph Skehel, M.L.M., M.B.I.M. Mr Donald Clark had resigned so as to devote full time to his business.

The Society's Lincolnshire Shows keep to the former principles, and express new ones. New or improved implements, for example, are judged as a century ago with regard to simplicity, low cost, and materials readily available to the farmer. At the same time as a new farriery building is provided, sporting and conservation are not neglected. Preference is given to agriculture in the demand for space, a new Ringside Club is provided for members, a tractor handling competition is revived, and the entertainment programme is augmented, young farmers are encouraged to plant trees, the small animals unit at Riseholme is sponsored. All is now expressed in the Society's new journal, The Lincolnshire.

Weather and science and the actions of government (and the E.E.C.) have been manœuvred by those who take pride in the Society and are active on its behalf. Success of recent years has resulted. A five-year record of greater attendance is succeeded by a six year record, and then a seventh. In the two days thirty thousand vehicles can arrive, carrying the equivalent of the population of a sizeable city, not one of whom wants delay in getting in and out. A questionnaire of 1,800 visitors in 1972 revealed that the majority were engaged in agriculture, with a major interest in livestock and demonstrations. These items are under annual consideration as ever. Adjustments to classification, and acceptance policy, and consequent support or otherwise of breeders, are part. But some years the weather can make harvest coincide with the Show, which results in absenteeism of stock because of labour shortage, which latter is ordinarily now not easy for animals from a distance away. The position was not helped by conditions on cattle handling and segregating being urged by the Ministry in 1969, conditions which were disputed as impracticable. Pigs are still sometimes absent due to swine versicular disease. Foot-and-Mouth can threaten. The weather hazard became too much for the crop demonstrations, tried with determination for a few years. While popular, results at the right time could by no means be guaranteed, nor is the land of the best for the purpose. Its value as a showground is its basic firmness, but for better crops it needs more top soil and more stone picking. And in 1982 three inches of rain (one eighth of the annual average) fell in the two days before the Show, and soon the avenues were deep in mud.

The one hundredth Show is this year, 1983. It is one stage in a continuous but adapting scene. Not only is the whole built upon the past, but also towards the future. The distribution of subjects among the members of the committee spreads the initiative: reception, ground and show displays, trade stands, cattle, horses, demonstrations, commissariat, sheep and pigs and their products, people and traffic, forestry.

In finance terms the early stock shows became maintained by implement companies joining in, and then retailers, who at first were related to farm and cottagers' needs. Members subscriptions kept the basic Society administration going, achieving further support from the locality of the Show. As folk became less related to agriculture they were drawn in by entertainment being added. More numbers brought more retailers, services, charities, and educative public bodies. Now the subscriptions and the revenue from lettings is approximately the development surplus.

Taking the money value of getting things done relative to what it used to be the Society is as buoyant as ever.

ONE HUNDRED LINCOLNSHIRE SHOWS
The Facts and Figures

Year	Venue	Attendance	Gate Receipts	Cattle	Sheep	Pigs	Horses	Trade Stands
1869	Lincoln		1,754	88	119	43	341	122
1870	Sleaford		1,122	95	119	46	250	108
1871	Brigg		1,177	110	94	61	271	109
1872	Spalding		2,360	118	109	74	280	125
1873	Gainsborough		1,155	148	111	78	252	92
1874	Grantham		1,844	118	140	94	292	99
1875	Grimsby		1,237	72	97	54	244	98
1876	Lincoln		1,822	102	123	50	282	114
1877	Boston		2,006	80	90	27	291	101
1878	Louth		1,771	86	93	38	284	109
1879	Stamford		1,168	84	103	55	221	109
1880	Brigg		996	61	69	35	198	90
1881	Lincoln		1,431	70	65	15	248	110
1882	Sleaford		1,172	71	73	31	238	106
1883	Gainsborough		706	71	60	42	229	92
1884	Grantham		1,320	111	94	56	242	108
1885	Grimsby		1,512	86	65	29	275	102
1886	Lincoln		1,085	84	75	54	379	190
1887	Spalding		1,172	104	68	40	280	—
1888			NO SHOW HELD					
1889	Louth	20,714	1,375	100	78	27	387	106
1890	Boston	22,419	1,635	90	91	55	350	106
1891	Brigg	13,752	908	75	75	33	279	89
1892	Lincoln	17,429	1,190	71	79	46	300	138
1893	Stamford	10,752	711	82	75	39	291	108
1894	Grimsby	19,649	1,297	58	61	—	272	127
1895	Grantham	15,257	1,040	51	68	50	342	145
1896	Gainsborough	14,768	918	69	81	36	310	114
1897	Sleaford	14,508	969	129	137	31	367	141
1898	Lincoln	20,890	1,293	120	127	37	222	144
1899	Louth	19,255	1,249	126	109	63	344	139
1900	Spalding	19,842	1,400	119	99	69	331	157
1901	Brigg	15,533	1,019	149	101	59	331	159
1902	Boston	22,683	1,455	152	73	37	359	171
1903	Lincoln	22,024	1,353	135	73	71	394	185

Year	Venue	Attendance	Gate Receipts	Cattle	Sheep	Pigs	Horses	Trade Stands
1904	Grimsby	26,535	1,646	182	72	84	424	183
1905	Grantham	15,582	985	145	81	79	451	152
1906	Gainsborough	20,473	1,022	164	81	83	386	139
1907	ROYAL SHOW HELD AT LINCOLN							
1908	Sleaford	13,302	947	221	101	124	489	153
1909	Louth	20,414	1,401	154	76	112	384	166
1910	Spalding	20,098	1,463	165	67	119	438	181
1911	Brigg	15,359	1,090	134	91	161	407	177
1912	Skegness	17,333	1,075	179	80	143	442	155
1913	Lincoln	29,231	1,818	139	98	110	531	196
1914	Boston	27,370	1,704	117	87	154	422	193
1915-1919	NO SHOWS HELD							
1920	Grimsby	40,719	6,126	105	79	66	289	136
1921	NO SHOW HELD							
1922	Skegness	22,598	3,539	88	56	97	238	123
1923	Lincoln	25,788	3,497	164	68	165	401	199
1924	Cleethorpes	20,576	2,653	108	70	160	342	139
1925	Grantham	20,647	2,183	144	80	157	378	177
1926	Louth	22,111	2,390	139	69	120	427	156
1927	Spalding	27,278	3,088	143	64	199	355	205
1928	Scunthorpe	26,433	2,669	154	81	147	300	166
1929	Sleaford	22,668	2,486	150	78	173	407	172
1930	Skegness		2,220	138	70	153	336	165
1931	Lincoln		2,225	127	55	155	344	181
1932	Grimsby	35,700	2,849	144	52	108	346	158
1933	Boston	30,433	2,834	139	37	136	374	181
1934	Gainsborough	23,970	2,283	151	45	160	389	161
1935	Grantham	18,293	1,920	173	53	152	447	163
1936	Louth	30,462	3,050	161	56	161	491	165
1937	Spalding	27,215	2,809	139	62	298	354	193
1938	Scunthorpe	29,972	2,788	143	90	266	440	163
1939	Bourne	20,343	2,275	143	62	338	271	163
1940-1945	NO SHOWS HELD							
1946	Blankney Park (one day)	12,214	1,526	139	58	132	315	40
1947	ROYAL SHOW HELD AT LINCOLN							
1948	Belton Park	17,337	3,408	159	97	327	413	137